TROILUS
and
CRISEYDE

"Alas, What is this wonderful malady?"

Geoffrey Chaucer's
TROILUS
and
CRISEYDE

Rendered into Modern English Prose

By R. M. LUMIANSKY, Professor of English, Tulane University

Illustrated by H. LAWRENCE HOFFMAN

*With a Portion of the Original
Middle English Text*

University of South Carolina Press
Columbia
1952

The Contents

The Illustrations

Introduction

I

Exactly when Geoffrey Chaucer (1340?-1400) wrote *Troilus and Criseyde* is not known; a date somewhere in the 1380's is probably the best guess. We do know, however, from the twenty manuscripts of the poem which have survived, that Chaucer must have labored long and carefully on the poem; in fact, three separate versions or stages of the work have been reconstructed from the manuscripts. But the clearest evidence of this careful work is the quality of the poem itself, for *Troilus and Criseyde* has been called Chaucer's "supreme example of sustained narration," and "the most perfect of his completed works."

For this story Chaucer was indebted primarily to Boccaccio's *Filostrato*, itself a poem of considerable distinction; yet the *Troilus* is by no means merely a retelling of Boccaccio's story. Rather, Chaucer found a relatively straightforward narrative in the *Filostrato*, which he expanded by various means into what is often called a "psychological novel." To accomplish this, among other things he complicated the plot, added philosophical themes, increased the medieval atmosphere, and spiced the dialogue with numerous bits of proverbial wisdom.

Chaucer's most important alteration of Boccaccio's poem, however, exists in his treatment of the three chief characters: Troilus, Criseyde, and Pandarus. In the Italian poem Troilo, Criseida, and Pandaro are fairly simple people whose motives and actions are, for the most part, easy to understand. But the nature of the three characters in Chaucer's poem is the subject for never-ending critical debate. Readers regularly raise—and seldom reach agreement upon—such questions as the following: Is Troilus to be sympathized with as an ideal courtly lover, or should we consider him a naive young man unable by his own efforts to win and hold the lady of his affections? Is Pandarus the conventional go-between who does all he can to further the happiness of his friend Troilus and his niece Criseyde, or is he seeking in the affair vicarious satisfaction to offset his own lack of success in love? Is Criseyde simply an unfaithful woman guided always by expediency, or can her desertion of Troilus be justified by her circumstances? And—in some ways most interesting of all—just how much is the reader's reaction to these three characters influenced by the Narrator's frequent expository comments and by his steadily sympathetic attitude toward Criseyde?

To answer such questions defensibly a reader needs first to understand something of the system of Courtly Love, a system which figured largely in the relationships between men and women of noble birth in late medieval literature. In its fundamentals this system is diametrically opposed to the teachings of the medieval Church, for marriage has no place in Courtly Love. Further, in this relationship, unlike the Sacrament of Marriage, the lady is in supreme authority and the lover is always considered her "servant." Included in the system of Courtly Love are numerous conventional acts and attitudes: the lover, smitten through the eyes, falls in love at first sight; he fears to make known his feeling to the lady; he suffers "the malady of love," as a result of which he cannot eat or sleep and cares nothing for his health or appearance; he writes highly emotional epistles to his lady; a go-between is the agent for urging the lover's case before the lady and for reporting her reactions to the lover; the lady holds aloof and yields with extreme reluctance; she assigns the lover difficult tasks through which he must prove the sincerity of his feeling for her; upon winning the lady, the lover is wonderfully ennobled and possesses all possible virtues and accomplishments; absolute secrecy must be maintained throughout the affair.

It will be immediately apparent to any reader that many aspects of Chaucer's *Troilus* can be accounted for by the system of Courtly Love. For example, Troilus falls in love at first sight; he suffers the malady of love and hesitates to inform Criseyde of his feeling; Criseyde is aloof and is finally won through the efforts of Pandarus as go-between; Criseyde insists on absolute secrecy, and Troilus is greatly ennobled by the relationship. But we should not overlook the fact that in certain important particulars *Troilus and Criseyde* differs markedly from the medieval Courtly Love romance. First, Criseyde is a widow, not a wife. Second, Pandarus is not only Troilus' friend but also Criseyde's uncle, and consequently has certain ethical responsibilities toward her. Third, the emphasis on secrecy stems not merely from conventional necessity but, more realistically, from Criseyde's feeling of insecurity in Troy as the daughter of the traitor Calchas.

By such pervasive alterations as these, Chaucer in *Troilus and Criseyde* went far beyond the conventional pattern and created in his three chief characters not stock figures but individuals who come alive and who thus furnish intellectual enjoyment and instruction on a universal scale. In the last analysis, it is through consideration of the motivation and action of these three individuals that *Troilus and Criseyde* becomes most meaningful.

II

Many authorities maintain that there is no need for a Modern English version of *Troilus and Criseyde,* or, in fact, of any of Chaucer's works. Chaucer's Middle English, they claii , is not very difficult to learn to read, and most of the charm and pleasure inherent in his poetry is lost when it is put into Modern English. Now it is certainly true that most of the charm of Chaucer's poetry is lost, or at least seriously lessened, by translation. But it is equally true—and the sales records of publishing houses prove this fact—that while Chaucer's poetry is very seldom read outside the schools in its Middle English original, a fairly extensive body of the general public will read his works in Modern English. I think that the inescapable conclusion to be drawn from this fact is that professional students of Chaucer's writings do well to make the best of his works available in Modern English, with the hope that readers will be led by the translations to Chaucer's original poems.

But even if one grants the conclusion stated above, there is a further, knottier problem to be met. In what sort of Modern English translation can *Troilus and Criseyde* be presented most effectively? In relatively recent years, J. S. P. Tatlock and Percy MacKaye chose archaic prose (Macmillan, 1912); G. P. Krapp chose rhyme-royal stanzas (Random House, 1932); and Theodore Morrison chose blank verse (Viking, 1949). As I see it, though each of these versions—especially Krapp's— was done with a high degree of skill and care, a better solution is to use Modern English prose. My reasons are as follows: First, Chaucer did not use archaic Middle English in *Troilus and Criseyde,* and purposely archaic Modern English prose is very hard to follow. Second, no recent translator of *Troilus and Criseyde* has been anywhere near so good a poet as Chaucer, and attention is inevitably invited to this sharp discrepancy when the medium is stanzaic or blank verse. Third, whereas the medieval reader or listener expected long narratives to be written in poetic form, the modern reader is accustomed to the use of prose for lengthy stories. Fourth, Chaucer's typical manner and tone, even in *Troilus and Criseyde,* can be more nearly reproduced in modern prose than in poetry.

The final problem in this connection has to do with selecting the most effective level of prose with which to represent *Troilus and Criseyde.* In the introductory remarks to my translation of the *Canterbury Tales* (Simon and Schuster, 1948), I argued that since in the *Canterbury Tales* Chaucer most frequently employed "the colloquial idiom of his day, using the humorous, direct, often slangy expressions which were heard on the busy streets of fourteenth-century London," the tone of the *Canterbury Tales* could therefore be most nearly reproduced through natural, idiomatic, colloquial Modern English prose. But the *Troilus* is an entirely different kind of book from the *Canterbury Tales.* Where the latter is swift, colorful, predominantly gay, and infinitely varied, the former is leisurely, for the most part sober, sustained, and highly introspective. Where the people in the latter are mostly middle class, in the former we have to do with the Trojan aristocracy. Consequently, colloquial, slangy, and highly idiomatic Modern English prose would impart a tone in no way suited to *Troilus and Criseyde.* Rather, I have tried to use what might be called semi-formal conversational Modern English, such as might be heard at a somewhat relaxed official function. It is true that at times—most often when Pandarus is speaking—we find a less elevated level; but in general a semi-formal conversational tone seems to me to fit the whole poem.

In making this translation, I have followed the text as it appears in F. N. Robinson's *Complete Works of Geoffrey Chaucer* (Houghton Mifflin, 1933), with regular attention to R. K. Root's *The Book of Troilus and Criseyde* (Princeton University Press, 1926). Readers who wish to learn more about *Troilus and Criseyde* will find the Introductions and Notes in these two editions extremely valuable. T. A. Kirby's *Chaucer's "Troilus": A Study in Courtly Love* (Louisiana State University Press, 1940) also illuminates numerous aspects of the poem.

R. M. L.

TROILUS
and
CRISEYDE

Here Begins Book I

MY purpose before leaving you is to recount the double sorrow in love experienced by Troilus, son of King Priam of Troy, and how in his adventures he passed from woe to happiness and afterwards to woe again. You, Tisiphone, help me to compose these woeful verses that weep even as I write them. I call upon you, cruel Fury, goddess of torment, sorrowing ever in pain, to aid me, a sorrowful instrument who helps lovers to bewail as best I can. For it is fitting, to tell the truth, that a sad person have a dreary comrade, and that a sad tale have a dreary tone. And I, who serve the servants of Love, dare not, because of my unsuitability, beg success from Love; so far am I in darkness from his help that I would die in such an effort.

Nevertheless, if my poem brings gladness to any lover and helps his cause, he may have my thanks and mine will be the labor. But you lovers who bathe in happiness, if there is any drop of pity in you, recall the past sadness you have known and the difficulty experienced by other folks, and remember how you have felt Love's displeasure—otherwise you won him over too easily—and pray for those who are in Troilus' situation, of which you will soon hear, so that Love may bring them to comfort in heaven. Pray also to dear God for me, so that I may have the power in some way to show by Troilus' unhappy adventure the pain and woe which Love's folk endure. Pray

3

Book One

also for those lovers so in despair that they will never recover, and for those men or women slandered by malicious tongues.

Pray God in His benignity to grant that those in despair for lack of Love's grace will soon pass from this world. Pray also for the happy ones, so that God will grant them continued bliss and send them the ability so to please their ladies that it will be a worship and a pleasure to Love. For I hope thus to bring profit to my soul by praying for Love's servants, by writing of their troubles, by living charitably, and by having compassion for them, as if I were their own dear brother. Now listen with good intent, for I shall go straight to my story in which you may hear Troilus' double sorrow in loving Criseyde, and how she forsook him before she died.

It is well known how the Greeks, powerful in arms, went towards Troy with a thousand ships and besieged the city for a long time—nearly ten years before they ceased—and with a single purpose though in various ways, they bent all their efforts to avenge the stealing of Helen by Paris. Now it happened that there was a lord of great authority, a great divine who was named Calchas, living in Troy; so expert in learning was he that he knew well from the replies of his god, Don Phebus or the Delphic Apollo, that Troy must be destroyed. So when this Calchas knew from his reckoning and also from Apollo's replies that the Greeks would bring such an army by which Troy would be demolished, he planned at once to leave the city. For he was sure from his astrological calculations that Troy was doomed, yes, no matter who liked it or disliked it. Consequently, this wise fore-knowing man determined to leave quietly, and soon he stole away secretly to the Greek camp;

and the Greeks courteously received him with dignity and worship, hoping that he had knowledge with which to counsel them in every danger which they feared.

When it was first noticed in Troy, and then became generally discussed, that Calchas had fled as a traitor and had allied himself with the Greeks, a clamor broke out and people laid plans to be avenged on him who had falsely broken faith; also they said that he and all his kin together deserved to be burned, skin and bones. Now in this unfortunate situation Calchas had left his daughter, who had no part in his false and wicked deed. She was very worried because she feared greatly for her life, and did not know what was best to do. For she was both a widow and without a friend to whom she dared turn for help.

This lady's name was certainly Criseyde. In my opinion there was no one so lovely in all Troy, for, surpassing everyone, so angelic was her natural beauty that she seemed like an immortal creature, as does a perfect heavenly being sent down to earth in scorn of Nature. This lady, who heard all day of her father's shame, his falseness and treachery, went almost out of her mind with sorrow and fear. In her widow's clothes of brown silk she fell down upon her knees before Hector; proclaiming her innocence and softly weeping, in a piteous voice she begged his help. Hector was sympathetic by nature, and observed both that she was overcome by sorrow and that she was a very beautiful person. In his kindness he at once cheered her and said, "Let your father's treason go its way with bad luck, and you yourself stay here happily with us in Troy as long as you wish. You shall have all the honor which men might have shown you if your father had continued to

Book One

live here. In so far as I can arrange it, you shall be fully protected."

She thanked him most humbly, and would have thanked him more if he had permitted it; then she took her leave, went home, and held her peace. At home she lived with a household befitting her station; as long as she dwelt in that city she maintained her dignity and was beloved by young and old, and everyone spoke well of her. But I have not read whether or not she had any children; therefore, I let it pass.

Things went on between the Greeks and Trojans, as they usually do in war: some days the Trojans paid dearly, and on other days the Greeks found their opponents by no means weak. Thus Fortune wheeled both of them first up then down, according to their courses, and all the while they were filled with anger. But it is not within my purpose to tell how this city came to destruction, for it would be a long digression from my present subject and would keep you too long. Anyone who is able may read about these events in the Trojan histories by Homer, Dares, or Dictys.

Although the Greeks had besieged Troy from all sides and thus enclosed the inhabitants, the Trojans would not abandon their old customs in devoutly honoring their gods. Without doubt, they held a relic called Palladium, in which they placed their greatest trust, in highest honor. Thus it happened when April ushered in the Spring, when the meadow is clothed with new green and the white and red flowers scent the air, that the folk of Troy, so I read, paid their ancient observances in various ways by holding the feast of the Palladium. Many a person went in his finest manner to the temple to hear the service of the Palladium, and especially were there many gay

Troilus and Criseyde

knights, handsome ladies, and fair maidens, every one—the rich, the poor, and the middle class—well-dressed both for the season and the feast.

In this crowd was Criseyde in a widow's black clothes; but, nevertheless, just as our first letter is now an A, so stood she matchless in beauty. Her fine appearance gladdened all the crowd. Never yet was there seen a person deserving higher praise, nor so bright a star behind a black cloud as was Criseyde —so everyone said who saw her in her black clothes. Yet she stood alone humbly and quietly behind the others in a little space near the door; she was constantly fearful of taunts, simply dressed, and debonair, with a confident gaze and manner.

Troilus, who was accustomed to guide his young knights, led them up and down about each side in the temple, always staring at the ladies of the town, now here, now there. He felt for no one lady a devotion which would steal from him his sleep; rather, he praised or found fault wherever he wished. As he walked about he watched carefully to see if any knight or squire in his company began to sigh or feast his eyes upon any woman present. In such a case Troilus would smile and consider it folly, and say, "God knows, for love of you she sleeps quietly, while you toss and turn! Indeed, I have heard about you lovers, about your way of living and your stupid customs; and of what a job people have in winning love, and of what perplexity in keeping it. And when your prey is gone, there is woe and penance. O, true fools, you are indeed stupid and blind! There is not a one who can learn from another's experience." With these words he raised his eyebrows as if to ask, "See, is not that wisely spoken?" At which the god of Love grew spitefully angry and began to prepare vengeance;

Book One

he soon gave proof that his bow was not broken, for suddenly he hit Troilus squarely. Truly Cupid can get the best of even those who are proud as a peacock.

O blind world, O blind purpose! How often does it happen that the result is exactly opposite to arrogant and foul presumption, for the proud are caught and the carefree as well. Now Troilus has climbed up the stairway and little does he think that he must descend. But every day those things fail in which fools put faith. When proud Bayard the horse is full of grain, he begins to skip out of the road until he feels a lash from the long whip; then he thinks, "Though I prance ahead as leader in the traces, fat and newly clipped, yet I am only a horse and I must endure a horse's lot and pull with my fellows." So it was with this haughty, proud knight; though he was the son of a noble king and thought that nothing had the power to stir his heart against his will, yet with one look his heart caught fire, so that he who was proudly aloof now became the most subjected to love.

All you wise, proud, noble folk, take this man as your example against scorning Love, which can so quickly enthrall the liberty of your hearts. For it was ever so and always shall be so that Love can conquer all things, since no man can overcome the laws of nature. That this is true has been and is often proved. For I think everybody knows that we read of no one possessed of greater intelligence than those who have been most subdued by Love; and the strongest, worthiest, and noblest folk are thus overcome. This always was so, and is, and ever shall be; and actually it should be so. For the wisest have been thus pleased, and those most woeful have been comforted and cheered by Love. Often Love has softened a cruel heart, and

8

Troilus and Criseyde

made worthy folk worthier, and caused them to fear vice and shame. Since Love cannot easily be withstood and is a thing naturally so powerful, do not refuse to be bound by Love, for, whenever he wishes, he can bind you. The rod which will sway and bend is better than that which breaks; therefore, I advise you to follow him who can so well lead you.

But to continue in detail about this king's son whom I mentioned, and to leave allied matters; I plan to go on with my tale of him, of both his joy and his cold cares. Since I began it, I shall complete his whole story.

Troilus went on amusing himself within the temple, staring at everyone, now at this lady, now at that one, no matter whether she was from the city or the surrounding countryside. By chance it happened that he looked through a crowd, and his glance fell upon Criseyde; there it stopped. Suddenly he became dazed and began to look at her more carefully. "O, mercy, God," he thought, "so fair and good to look upon, where have you been?" At this his heart began to swell and rise; he sighed softly, for fear men would hear him, and resumed his former playful manner. She was not particularly small in stature, but all her limbs so approached womanly perfection that there was never a creature of less masculine appearance. The dignity with which she moved showed clearly that one could guess that she possessed honor, rank, and feminine nobility. Troilus, wonderingly, began to like her manner and appearance, which was somewhat disdainful, for she let her glance fall a bit to one side, as if to say, "What, may I not stand here?" Then her face lighted up and it seemed to him that he had never seen so fine a sight. From her glance such great desire and affection quickened within him that the deep

Book One

and fixed impression of her stuck in the bottom of his heart. Though earlier he had looked boldly up and down at random, now he was glad to let his horns shrink in; he scarcely knew how to look or wink.

See, he who thought himself so clever and scorned those who suffer Love's pains, was completely unaware that Love had his dwelling-place within the subtle beams from her eyes. It seemed to him that he felt the spirit in his heart suddenly die at one glance from her. Blessed be Love who can thus convert folk! Troilus stood looking at this lady in black who pleased him above all things. He gave no sign and said no word to indicate his desire or why he stood thus. But to maintain his former manner, he occasionally cast his eyes on other far-off things, then back to her, as long as the service lasted. Afterwards, somewhat amazed, he quietly went from the temple, regretting that he had ever joked about Love's servants, for fear the weight of scorn should fall heavily on him. He carefully hid and concealed the pain which he felt, lest it become in any way known.

When he thus left the temple he at once turned towards his palace, pierced through and wounded by Criseyde's look; yet he still pretended to live in gaiety. He brightened his manner and speech and, to conceal his feelings, he laughed now and then at Love's servants, saying, "Lord, how happily you lovers live! For the cleverest of you, he who serves most attentively and best, as often receives harm as profit. Your efforts are justly repaid; yes, God knows how! Not good for good, but scorn for good service. In faith, your fraternity is ruled in fine fashion! All your rites are based on uncertainty, except perhaps for a few unimportant points. Yet no faith requires such

10

steady devotion as yours, and all of you know that well. But that is not the worst thing, as I hope to prosper! If I told you the worst—I think, if I spoke truly—you would be aggrieved with me. But take this as an example: that which you lovers frequently avoid or perform with good intentions is often misconstrued by your ladies and considered wrong by them. Yet if your lady for another reason is angry, then will you begin to groan at once. Lord, a man who is one of your number is really happy!"

Despite all this, when he saw his time he held his peace; no other remedy helped him. For Love had so limed his feathers that he was barely able to pretend to his followers that other worries oppressed him. He was so woebegone that he did not know what to do, but bade his followers go where they liked. When he was alone in his room, he sat down on the foot of his bed; first he began to sigh, then to groan, and thought steadily without interruption about Criseyde, so that as he sat there wide awake his spirit dreamed that he saw her in a temple; he saw all the details of her features and began to consider them anew. Thus he made a mirror of his mind in which he saw her whole figure.

He found it in his heart to admit that it was good fortune for him to love such a one, and that if he did his best to serve her he might win her favor, or at least be considered one of her suitors. He decided that labor and tribulation would not be wastefully expended for one so fine as she, and that his desire would reflect no shame on him even if it became known; rather, he would be honored and exalted by all lovers more than before. Thus in the beginning he reasoned, wholly unaware of his coming tragedy; and thus he determined to follow

Book One

Love's craft, but planned to work quietly in order to hide his desire completely from everyone, so that he might profit somewhat thereby. He called to mind that love too widely broadcast yields bitter fruit, even though sweet seed are sown. In addition, he thought much more about what to talk of and what to keep within him, and how to urge her to love him. Immediately he began a song and sang loudly to overcome his sorrow, for he was now fully decided to love Criseyde with strong hope, and to regret it not at all.

I am quite willing to give you, just as Troilus sang it, not only the meaning, but also the text of Troilus' song, as written down by my author Lollius, except for the difference in languages. Look, every word was just as I shall say it, and whoever wishes to see it, he may find it here in the next stanzas.

THE SONG OF TROILUS

If no love exists, O God, what feel I so?
If love exists, what thing and which is it?
If love is good, what causes my grief?
If it is evil, I find it strange
That every torment and difficulty
Which comes of it can seem to me sweet;
For I thirst always, the more of love I drink.

And if I burn from my own desire,
Whence come my wailing and complaint?
If grief pleases me, then why do I complain?
I do not know, nor why I faint unwearied.
O living death, O sweet grief so strange,
How can there be in me so much of you
Unless I consent that it be so?

12

Troilus and Criseyde

And if I consent, then surely wrong am I
To complain. Thus shuttled to and fro
Rudderless within a boat am I
In the midst of the sea, between two winds,
Which stand contrary evermore.
Alas! What is this wondrous malady?
Of heat in cold, or cold in heat, I die.

Then to the god of Love Troilus spoke in a piteous voice: "O, lord, my spirit which ought to be yours is now yours. Lord, I thank you, who have brought me this. Actually, I do not know whether she whom you cause me to serve is a goddess or a woman, but I will live forever and die her man. You stand clearly in her eyes, as a place befitting your power. Therefore, lord, if I or my service please you, be kind to me, for I hereby resign my royal rank into her hands, and in all humility become her man, as she is my dear lady."

The fire of love, from which God keep me, did not deign to spare Troilus' royal blood, nor to treat him at all tenderly because of his prowess or great strength; rather it held him low as a thrall in distress, and burned him continuously in various ways so that his cheeks paled sixty times a day. Day by day his own thoughts so quickened and stirred in desire for her that he cared nothing for all his other responsibilities.

Very often, in order to cool his hot desire, he strove to catch a glimpse of her lovely features, for he thought he would be comforted thereby; but ever the nearer he was, the more he burned. For ever the nearer the fire, the hotter one grows— this, I trust, everyone here realizes. But whether he was far or near, I dare say this: by day or night, for wisdom or folly, his

13

heart, which is the eye of his breast, was always on Criseyde, who was fairer to see than Helen or Polyxena ever was. Also not an hour of the day passed but what he said to himself a thousand times, "Good fair one, Criseyde, whom I serve and labor for as best I can, now would to God that you would take pity on me before I die! Dear heart, alas, my health, appearance, and life are lost unless you pity me."

All other fears, both of the siege and his own well-being, fled from him. In him desire bred no other offspring than arguments to this conclusion: she would have compassion on him and he would be her man as long as he lived. So—there was his life and his surety against death. The brilliant, dangerous feats at arms performed by Hector or his other brothers moved Troilus not the slightest; yet wherever men walked or rode he was bound to be one of the best, and he remained longest where there was danger and did such work in the fighting that it was marvelous to think about.

But his rage in battle was not inspired by the hatred he bore the Greeks nor by a wish to rescue the city; indeed, only by this cause: to please Criseyde better with his fame. From day to day he fought so valiantly that the Greeks feared him as death. From this time on, love kept him from his sleep and made his food his enemy. His sorrow multiplied so that, if one were observant, it was always apparent, night and day, in his face. Therefore, he began to borrow the name of another illness, lest men think that the hot fire of love burned him; and he said that he had a fever and fared badly. But I cannot really state whether his lady failed to understand his pretense or feigned ignorance of it—one or the other. Yet I did read that it seemed in no way that she cared about him, his pain, or whatever he thought.

Then Troilus felt such woe that he was nearly insane; for his constant fear was this: she was so in love with another man that she would never take heed of him. On account of this, it seemed to him that his heart bled, yet for all the world he dared not begin to tell her of his torment. When he experienced a brief respite from his grief, he often complained thus to himself: "O fool, now you who once joked at the pangs of love are caught in the trap. Now you are trapped; now gnaw through your own chains! You were always accustomed to reprimand each lover for a thing from which you cannot defend your own self. If this is known, what will every lover say about you now? Behind your back they will laugh in scorn and say, 'See, there goes the man of such great wisdom who considered us lovers least deserving of reverence. Now, thank God, he may join the dance with those whom Love decides to aid least. But, O woeful Troilus, God willed that since you were destined to fall in love, you were smitten by one who, knowing your woe, withheld all her pity! Your lady is as cold in love for you as frost under a winter moon, and you will be destroyed as rapidly as snow in the fire.'

"Would to God I had arrived in the haven of death, to which my sorrow will lead me! Ah, Lord, it would be a great comfort to me; then would I have finished this languishing in fear. For, if my hidden sorrow becomes rumored abroad, I shall be laughed at a thousand times more than that fool whose folly is the subject for men's rhymes. Now help me, God, and you also, sweet one for whom I pine; I am caught, yes, tighter than any man before me! O mercy, dear heart, and keep me from

Book One

death, for as long as I live I will love you more than myself. Cheer me, sweet one, with a friendly glance, even though you promise me no more."

He spoke these words, together with many others, and constantly repeated her name in his complaint, in order to tell her of his woe, until he almost drowned in his own salty tears. All was in vain: she did not hear his plea. When he realized his folly, his grief increased a thousandfold. As he thus lamented alone in his room, a friend of his, who was named Pandarus, came in unannounced and, hearing his groaning, saw his friend in such distress and worry.

"Alas," said Pandarus, "who caused all this to-do? O mercy, God, what misfortune does this indicate? Have the Greeks so quickly caused you to lose weight? Or have you some remorse of conscience which has made you so devout that you now bewail your sins and faults and have shrunk with fear? Surely God should bless the besiegers of our city if they can so end our enjoyment of the world and bring our lusty folk to holiness!" Pandarus spoke all these words for the specific purpose of making Troilus angry, in the hope that such anger would replace his woe for the time being and raise his spirits. But he knew well that wherever people talked there was no man deemed of greater courage or more desirous of glory than Troilus.

"What purpose or what chance has led you here to see me languishing and rejected by every creature?" asked Troilus. "For the love of God, I pray you, go away from here; surely you will be infected by my death, and I must certainly die. Therefore, go away; there is no more to be said. But if you think that I am ill from fear, you are wrong; so don't speak

16

Troilus and Criseyde

scornfully. There is another thing which bothers me far more than anything the Greeks have yet done, and which will cause my death from sorrow and worry. But do not be angry because I tell you nothing about it; I conceal it for the best."

Pandarus, almost melting with grief and pity, said repeatedly, "Alas, what can this be? Now, friend, if ever there was, or if there is, love or trust between you and me, do not ever be so cruel as to hide from your friend the cause of your trouble! Don't you realize it is I, Pandarus? If it happens that I cannot comfort you, I will share all your pain. Truly it is a friend's right to share pain as well as pleasure. I have loved you and shall all my life, in wrong and right and in the face of true or false reports. Don't hide your woe from me; tell it quickly."

Then the unhappy Troilus sighed and said to him, "God grant that it is best for me to tell you, for since you wish it I shall tell you about it, though my heart may break. I know well that you cannot comfort me; but, lest you think I do not trust you, now listen, friend, here is the way it stands with me: Love, against whom the man who defends himself most accomplishes least, oppresses me so sorrowfully with despair that my heart sails straight towards death. I am so hotly consumed by desire that to be killed would be a greater pleasure for me than to be king of Greece and Troy. My dear friend Pandarus, let that which I have said suffice, for now you know my trouble. For the love of God, hide well my grievous concern—I have told it to no other. If it were known, more than two evils might result. But continue happy, and let me die unknown · in my distress."

Book One

"You fool," said Pandarus, "how have you unnaturally hidden this from me so long? Perhaps you pine for a person concerning whom my advice would be immediately helpful to us."

"That would be a miraculous thing," replied Troilus. "You could never help yourself in love; how the devil can you bring me to happiness?"

"Yes, now listen, Troilus," Pandarus answered; "though I am foolish, it often happens that one who fares very badly through excess can by good advice keep his friend away from the same fault. I myself have also seen a blind man walking safely where a man with good eyesight fell down. Then, too, a fool may often guide a wise man. A whetstone is not a carving instrument; yet it makes carving tools sharp. Where you know that I have made mistakes, avoid them; let them be as school for you. Thus are wise men often taught by fools.

"If you do that, you will be well warned; each thing is known by its opposite. For how could sweetness ever have been known by one who had not tasted bitterness? No man may be fully happy, I think, who was never somewhat in sorrow or distress. Also white by black and shame by worth are made known. Each is heightened by contrast with the other and thereby made more evident; thus a wise man reasons. Since two opposites set up one conclusion, I who have so often suffered grievances in love ought to be better able to counsel you concerning that by which you are distressed. Also you ought not be evilly rewarded if I wish to share with you your heavy burden; it will be less heavy. I know well that things go with me just as a shepherdess, who was named Oënone, wrote to your brother Paris when she complained of her grief; you saw the letter she wrote, I think."

18

Troilus and Criseyde

"No, not yet," said Troilus.

"Then listen," said Pandarus, "it went this way: 'Phebus, who founded the art of medicine, knew a remedy and cure by means of some fine herb for everyone's trouble; yet his skill was useless for himself. Love for the daughter of King Admetus had so ensnared him that all his cunning could not remedy his grief.' Just so, unfortunately, is it with me. I love one best and am sorely grieved by it. Yet perhaps I can advise you though not myself; mock me no more. I have no cause, I know, to soar like a hawk in play, but I can suggest something to help you. You can be absolutely sure of one thing: I will never give away your secret though I die in pain for it; nor, on my honor, do I care to dissuade you from your love, even if I knew it were Helen, who is your brother's wife. Let her be what she is; love her as you wish! Therefore, trust fully in me as your friend. Tell me exactly the reason and the final cause of the woe you suffer. Doubt nothing; my intention is not to reprimand you now, for no one can lead another from love until he wishes to give it up.

"Understand clearly that both are vices: to mistrust everyone, or else to believe everyone. But I am sure that the middleway is not a vice, for to trust some person is a proof of faith; and for that reason I am eager to correct your wrong decision and cause you to trust someone by telling me your trouble. Now tell me if you wish. The wise say, 'Woe to him who is alone, for if he falls he has no help in rising.' Since you have a friend, tell your grief. For surely it is not the best way to win love—so the wise tell us—to wail and weep like Queen Niobe whose tears may still be seen in marble. Stop your

Book One

weeping and your sadness; let's lighten woe by other talk. Your period of sadness will thus seem shorter.

"Do not delight in covering your woe with woe, as these fools do who, when they suffer misfortune, add sorrow to sorrow and do not listen in seeking some other remedy. Men say, 'It is a consolation to a miserable creature to have a companion in his torment.' That should certainly be our opinion, for both you and I complain of love. To tell the truth, I am so full of sorrow that certainly no more hard luck may fall upon me; there is no room for it. God knows you are not afraid that I will steal your lady from you! Indeed, you know yourself whom I have loved as best I can for a long time. Since you know I plan no trick—and you say I am he whom you most trust—then tell me something, for you are familiar with all my woes."

Despite all this Troilus said not a word, but lay for a long time as still as if he were dead. Then he sighed loudly, gave his attention to Pandarus' voice, and so cast up his eyes that Pandarus was frightened lest he fall into a frenzy or else quickly die.

"Wake up!" Pandarus cried, fearfully and sharply. "What, are you sleeping in a lethargy, or are you like an ass with a harp: he hears the sound when the strings are plucked but the melody cannot sink into his mind to gladden him, because he in his bestiality is too stupid?"

With that Pandarus ceased talking; but Troilus still made no answer because his intention was to tell no man who caused his grief. For it is said by the wise that "A man often makes a rod with which the maker himself is in various ways beaten." Especially, this is seen in a man's confidential telling of matters

Troilus and Criseyde

concerning love which ought to be secret. For enough will come to light of itself, unless it is carefully guarded. Also it is sometimes wise to seem to run away from a thing which men usually hunt diligently. All these ideas Troilus turned over in his mind.

Nevertheless, when he heard Pandarus cry "Awake," he began to sigh deeply and said, "Friend, though I lie still, I am not deaf. Now peace, and shout no more, for I have heard your speech and counsel. But permit me to bewail my ill-luck; your proverbs cannot help me at all. Nor can you offer me any other remedy. Also I do not wish to be cured; I wish to die. What do I know of Queen Niobe? Stop quoting your ancient examples, I pray you."

"Well," said Pandarus, "it is just as I observed. Fools take delight in bewailing their troubles, but they do not try to find a remedy. Now I know that your ability to reason is failing. But tell me, am I acquainted with this lady who causes you all this grief? Would you dare let me whisper your feeling to her, since you don't dare to do it yourself, and beg her to have some pity on you?"

"Why, no, by God and my faith," replied Troilus.

"What," asked Pandarus, "not even if I do it as carefully as if my own life depended on it?"

"Certainly not, brother," replied Troilus.

"Now why?" asked Pandarus.

"Because you would not be successful," said Troilus.

"Are you sure of that?" inquired Pandarus.

"Yes, without doubt," said Troilus; "in spite of all your efforts she will never be won by such a wretch as I."

"Alas," said Pandarus, "how can it be that you are so deep in

Book One

despair without cause? Why, bless me, isn't your lady still alive? How do you know that you are without hope of her favor? Such a bad situation is not always incurable. Why, do not consider success an impossibility for you, for future events are often settled by chance. I grant indeed that you suffer woes as bitter as those of Tityus in hell, whose stomach birds called vultures constantly tear, as the books relate. But I cannot permit you to continue in so unfounded a conclusion as that there is no cure for your ailment. Will you not, despite your cowardice, ire, foolish wilfulness, and lack of faith, tell your troubles just once and make an effort to help yourself by the mere utterance of a few words, rather than lie here like one who cares for nothing?

"What woman could love such a wretch? What can she conclude from your death, if you die now, when she does not know why, but that you gave up life from fear of the Greeks who now besiege us? Lord, what a reward that would be for your suffering! Then will she say, together with the whole city, 'The wretch is dead; the devil take his bones!' You may weep, cry, and kneel here alone, but love a woman without her knowing it and she will repay you without your feeling it. That which is unknown is unkissed, and that unsought lost. Why, many a man has given twenty years to a lady who knew of his love, and yet has never received a kiss in return. Should he therefore fall into despair, or be cowardly to his own hurt, or slay himself, even though his lady is fair? No, no, he should be ever fresh and gay in the service of the dear queen of his heart, and think it a reward to serve her a thousandfold greater than he deserves."

Troilus and Criseyde

Troilus gave heed to these words and at once thought of the folly into which he had fallen; it seemed to him that Pandarus spoke truly in saying that to kill himself was not to profit but rather to do an unmanly act and to sin; his lady would know nothing of his death, since, God knows, she knew nothing about his woe. With that thought he sighed sorely and said, "Alas, what is best for me to do?"

Pandarus answered, "If it pleases you, the best is to tell me all your trouble; you have my promise that, unless you find I can help you in the near future, you can have me drawn and then hanged!"

"Yes, so you say," replied Troilus, "but, God knows, it is not therefore true. It will be hard to help me in this matter because I find that Fortune is my enemy. Not all the men who walk or ride can stand against the harm caused by her cruel wheel. For she plays as she likes with the free and the bound."

"Now I finally begin to see," said Pandarus; "you blame Fortune for your situation. Don't you know very well that every man, whatsoever his station, is subject to Fortune? And, indeed, you still have this comfort: just as her joys must vanish, so must every one of her sorrows pass away. For if her wheel stopped its turning, then she would cease to be Fortune. Now, since her wheel may in no way stop turning, how do you know that her instability will not bring about for you exactly what you wish, or that she is not far from helping you? Perhaps you have cause to sing. Therefore, do you know what I beg of you? Put aside your woe and downcast manner, for whoever hopes to have help from his doctor, it behooves him first to unwrap his wound. Even if you were so woebegone because of my sister, may I be forever chained to Cerberus in hell, if

Book One

I would not do all I could to make her yours tomorrow. Look up, I say, and tell me at once who she is so that I can commence helping you. Do I know her at all? Tell me this as reward for my love, and then I can hope to be successful."

Then Troilus' blood began to pound, for he was hit, and he turned all red with shame. "Aha," said Pandarus, "here begins the sport." With these words he started shaking Troilus and said, "Thief, you must tell her name." But then poor Troilus began to tremble as though men were leading him to hell, and he said, "Alas, the source of all my woe is my sweet enemy called Criseyde!" At the name he almost died of fear.

When Pandarus heard her name, Lord, he was happy, and said, "Dear friend, now surely, by Jove in heaven, Love has done well by you. Cheer up! For she has sufficient reputation, wisdom, dignity, and courtesy. You know yourself, I believe, whether or not she is fair. I never saw one of her station more generous, nor a happier one, nor one in speech more friendly, nor one more gracious and sure of the fitting thing to do; and as for honor, to cap all her other qualities, a king's heart seems that of a wretch beside hers. Therefore you should be comforted, for certainly the first characteristic of a noble and well ordered spirit is for a man to be at peace with himself. So should it be with you because it is in no way an evil thing to love one well who deserves your love. You should not call it chance but the grace of God. Think also, and rejoice therefore, that since your lady possesses all the virtues, some pity must be among them. Consequently, be especially sure that you ask nothing which will hurt her reputation, for virtue will not countenance shame.

24

Troilus and Criseyde

"I am happy that I was born to see your love so well placed. By my troth, I would have dared to swear that you could never have been so fortunate. Do you know why? Because you were wont to scoff at Love, and for spite to call him 'Saint Idiot, lord of all these fools.' How often you made these foolish jokes and said that the servants of Love were every one true apes of God in their folly; and some would munch their food alone lying abed and bewailing, and others, you said, had green-sickness, and you prayed God they wouldn't recover. Because of cold some of them put too much over them in bed, you often remarked. And some many times pretended to lie awake when they slept soundly. Thus they strove to rise aloft, but nevertheless were underneath in the end. So you said, and joked heartily. Also you said that these lovers, for the most part, urged their affection on everyone, and thought it a sure protection against failure to try everywhere.

"But now I can laugh at you if I wish; yet though I should die for it I dare say that you are not one of the last group. Now beat your breast and say to the god of Love, 'I beg your grace, lord, and now repent if I spoke wrongly, for now I myself am in love.' Speak thus with all your heart and good intentions."

Troilus said, "Ah, lord, I agree, and pray you to forgive my jokes; and never again so long as I live will I repeat them."

"You speak well," said Pandarus; "and now I hope that you have appeased all the god's wrath. Since you have wept many tears and spoken pleasing things to your god, I pray to the Lord that you will be comforted! Think of this: she who is the cause of all your woe may in the future also be your comfort. For the same ground which bears wicked weeds also bears wholesome herbs; often the rose grows sweet, smooth, and soft right next to the foul, rough, thick nettles. Beside the valley is the high hill; after the dark night comes the bright morning; and joy is nearest the end of sorrow. Be sure that the bridle is always loose enough to let the horse have his head; otherwise, all our labor is useless: he hastens well who wisely can wait. Be diligent and true; conceal all well; be lusty and generous; persevere in your suit; and all will be well, if you work in this fashion.

"But he who is parted in every place is nowhere whole, the clerics say. What wonder is it if such a one does not find favor? Also you know how it goes in some love-affairs: just as if one planted a tree in some place, and then pulled it up the next morning! No wonder it can never thrive. Since the God of Love has placed you in keeping with your nobility, stand fast, for you have rowed into a good port. Hope well for yourself, despite any sadness, for, unless pessimism or too great haste ruins our work, I hope to bring this to a good end. Do you know why I am not in the least afraid to discuss this matter with my niece? I have heard wise, learned men say that there was never a man or woman born who was not willing to suffer the heat of love, either celestial or natural. Therefore, I hope to win some favor from her. In her particular case, considering her beauty and youth, it is not likely that she would as yet be celestial, even if she could and would. Truly, it is quite fitting now for her to love and cherish a worthy knight; unless she does so, I consider it a vice. Therefore, I am and ever will be ready to take pains in serving you in this matter; I hope to please both of you in the future.

Troilus and Criseyde

"You are both discreet and can keep your own counsel in such a way that no man will be the wiser. Thus we all three may be made happy. On my word I have now formed a good picture of you in my mind, I think, and I want you to see what it is. I think that since Love in his goodness has converted you from your error, you shall now be the best pillar in all his cult and grieve his enemies most. Take as an example how these wise clerics who sin most greatly against their laws, and are then converted from their wicked ways by the grace of God, who wishes to draw them to Him, become the folk with strongest faith who hold God in greatest awe and, I am told, can best withstand sin."

When Troilus heard Pandarus consent to help him win Criseyde, his woe ceased tormenting him but his love waxed hotter; he said seriously, though his heart danced, "Now, may blessed Venus be of such help that before I die I may deserve your thanks, Pandarus. But, dear friend, how shall my woe decrease until this is ended? And, also, friend, tell me this: how will you speak of me and my distress without angering her—certainly I fear that most—so that she will not listen to or believe what you say? I fear all this, and also because of your position as her uncle she will not listen to such a matter."

Pandarus said, "You would worry about the man falling out of the moon! Lord, I hate your foolish chatter! Why, think about that which you have to do! For the love of God, I ask a favor of you: leave me alone and it will be for the best."

"Why, friend," said Troilus, "do just as you wish. But listen to one thing, Pandarus: I do not want you to attribute to me such great folly as to desire for my lady anything connected with harm or vulgarity. For without doubt, I would rather die than have her think anything of me which was not honorable."

Then Pandarus laughed and at once answered, "Am I your guarantee? Fie, no lover thinks otherwise than you. I wish she had been standing nearby to hear what you said! But farewell, I must go. Adieu! Be happy! God speed us both! Leave the labor and trouble to me, and the sweetness from my success will be all yours."

Then Troilus fell to his knees, clasped Pandarus tightly in his arms and said, "Now, to the devil with all the Greeks! Indeed, in the end God will help us, and without doubt if God is willing, and if my life lasts, I will make some of them smart. But I am sorry I gave voice to that boast. Now, Pandarus, I can say no more, except that you are wise, you know all, you can do all, you are all! I place my life and death completely in your hands. Now help me!"

"On my word, I shall," said Pandarus.

"God reward you, friend," said Troilus, "especially if you can recommend me to her who can command my death."

This Pandarus, desirous now of serving his friend fully, said, "Farewell, and remember that I am going to deserve your thanks! You have my word, and you shall soon see." Then he went his way thinking over the problem: how he best might beg her favor, at what time, and where. For every man who must build a house does not rush with rash hands to begin the work; rather, he should wait a bit and send out his heart's line to determine first his plan. Pandarus thought about all this and wisely planned his work before beginning.

Troilus and Criseyde

Troilus lay in bed no longer; at once he mounted his bay horse and played the lion on the battlefield. Woe was that Greek who met him on this day! From then on his manner in the city was so proper and won him so much favor that everyone who saw his face loved him. For he became the friendliest, gentlest, most generous, and thriftiest person, and also one of the best knights that there was or could be in his time. Gone were his jokes and his cruelty, his haughtiness and distant manner, and each of these was replaced by a virtue.

Now let us leave Troilus for a while, who fares like a man sorely hurt who is somewhat healed of the ache from his wound, but not completely cured. Like a comfortable patient, he looks forward to instructions from him who prepares the cure. Thus he carries forward his adventure.

HERE ENDS BOOK I

Here Begins Book II

wind, O wind, the weather begins to clear so that I can sail out of these black waves, for the boat has had such labor in the sea that, despite my skill, I could hardly steer it. The tumultuous despair which Troilus experienced I call the sea. But now the hopeful period commences.

O my lady Clio, be my helper and Muse henceforth to rhyme well in this book until I finish it. I need here no other art than yours. Therefore, I make excuses to every lover, for the sentiments here expressed are not mine; I am translating from Latin into English. Thus, I desire neither thanks nor blame for this work, but meekly pray you not to blame me if the words are awkward; for as my author says, so say I.

It is no wonder that I speak of love unfeelingly; such an attitude is not new, for a blind man cannot tell colors well. You know also that there have been changes in the forms of speech within a thousand years, and words then highly esteemed are now considered by us wondrously strange and foolish; and yet in those days they spoke so, and sped as well in love as men do now. Also, in various lands during various ages the customs for winning love have been various. Consequently, I do not know whether there happens to be any lover present listening to this story of how Troilus came into his lady's favor, and then thinking "I would not win love that

30

Troilus and Criseyde

way," or being surprised at Troilus' speech or his actions; but to me it would not be surprising, for every man who goes to Rome does not follow the same road or the same procedure. Also, in some countries the game would be wholly lost if men followed the same system in love that is usual here; for example, in frankness or in appearance, in visiting, manners, or in speaking. It is for that reason that men say each country has its own laws. Further, even here there are scarcely three people who have said and done everything the same way in love. For one thing may suit your purpose well, but the next man's not at all; in fact, every way is tried by someone. Also some men engrave in a tree and some in a stone wall, as they wish; but since I have so begun, I shall continue to follow my author, if I am able.

In May, the mother of the happy months, when the budding blue, white, and red flowers which winter killed are revived and every meadow is floating in balmy air, when Phebus spreads his bright beams from the white Bull, it happened as I shall now relate:

On May third Pandarus, despite all his wise speeches, also felt so keenly the thrusts of love that, no matter how well he could preach about love, he turned green many times that day. It happened that there came to him that day so great a love-pang that he woefully went to bed and tossed about many a time before dawn came. The swallow Progne began with a sorrowful song to make her lament at dawn, telling why she suffered metamorphosis. Pandarus still lay in bed, half asleep, until she came so near him with her chatter of how Tereus carried away her sister that the noise awakened him. He called to his servants and prepared to get up, remembering

Book Two

the errand he must do for Troilus and also his great responsibility. He knew by astrological reckoning that the moon was well placed for his effort, and he immediately made his way to his niece's palace nearby. Now Janus, god of entrance, guide him!

When he arrived at the palace he asked Criseyde's servants, "Where is my lady?" They told him, and he entered and found two other ladies sitting with her in a paved parlor; the three were listening to a girl reading them the romance of the siege of Thebes. Pandarus said, "Madam, God save you, your fine book, and your company!" Criseyde answered, "Ah, welcome, my uncle," and rose. Clasping his hand firmly she said, "Three nights ago—may it turn to profit—I dreamed of you." With these words she seated him on a bench.

"Yes, niece, you'll fare much better for it, if God wills, all this year," said Pandarus. "But I am sorry to keep you from listening to this book you praise so. For love of God, what is it about? Tell us! Is it of love? O, teach me something worthwhile!"

"Uncle," she replied, "your mistress is not here." With that, everybody began to laugh, and then she said, "This romance we are reading is about Thebes, and we have heard how King Laius died through Oedipus his son, and all those things. We stopped here at these red letters where the book tells how the bishop Amphiaraus fell through the earth to hell."

"I know all this myself, and all the siege of Thebes and the troubles," said Pandarus; "for twelve books have been made of that material. But put this aside and tell me how it is with you; remove your neck-piece and show your face. Put away your book, rise, and let's dance to do honor to May."

Troilus and Criseyde

"I? God forbid!" said Criseyde. "Are you insane? Is that the life for a widow, God save you? By God, you frighten me terribly! You are so reckless you seem to rave. It would be far more fitting for me to remain always in a cavern and read holy saints' lives; let maidens and young wives go dance."

"But as I hope to thrive," said Pandarus, "I could tell you something which would make you gay."

"Then, dear uncle," she said, "tell it to us, for the love of God. Is the siege lifted? I am so afraid of the Greeks that I die."

"No, no," answered Pandarus; "as I hope to prosper, it's a thing much better than five like that."

"Holy God, indeed; what can it be?" she asked. "What? Better than five such? For me, certainly not! I cannot for all the world guess what it could be; some joke, I think it is. Unless you tell us what it is, my wits are too slim to solve it. So help me God, I don't know what you mean."

"And I guarantee you, you never will know this thing from me, as I hope to thrive!" said Pandarus.

"Why not, uncle? Why not?" she asked.

"By God," he replied, "I'll soon tell you why not! Because there is no prouder woman alive in all the city of Troy, if you only knew it. I don't joke, as I hope to be happy!"

Then she began to wonder a thousand times more than before, and cast her eyes down. For never since the time that she was born had she desired to know any thing so much. But with a sigh she said at last to him, "Now, uncle, I shall not displease you by asking further that you do something against your will." So, after this, with many gay words, friendly tales, and happy looks, they played at this or that. They went into many a secret matter, trivial or serious, as friends do when they meet. Finally, she asked him how it was with Hector, who was the city's wall and the scourge of the Greeks.

"Very well, thank God," said Pandarus, "except that he has a small wound in his arm. All goes well with his lively brother Troilus, also, the wise worthy Hector the second, in whom all virtues abound: truth, courtesy, wisdom, honor, freedom, and nobility."

"In good faith, uncle, it pleases me," she said, "that they both are well; God save both of them! For truly I consider it a rare thing for a king's son to do well in battle, and to be fitted for war. Seldom are great power and moral virtue here seen united in one person."

"In good faith, that is true," said he. "But on my word, the king has two sons—I mean Hector and Troilus—who I am certain, though I should die, are as lacking in vices, I dare say, as any men living under the sun. Their strength and what they can do are widely known. There is no need to say anything else about Hector: in all the world there is no better knight than he, who is the well of all nobility; he has many other virtues in addition to strength. Many wise and noble people know this. I hold the same high opinion of Troilus. So help me God, I don't know another such two."

"By God," she said, "that is true of Hector; I think it is the same with Troilus. For, without doubt, men say that he performs so nobly in battle day by day and conducts himself so courteously toward everyone here at home, that he has the full praise of those by whom I would most desire to be praised."

"Certainly, you speak truly," said Pandarus. "Whoever had happened to be with Troilus yesterday would have been

Troilus and Criseyde

amazed at him, for never was there a swarm of bees or flies so thick as the Greeks who fled before him, and throughout the battlefield, in everyone's ears, rang only the cry, 'Troilus is there!' Now here, now there, he hunted them so fast that there was nothing but Greeks' blood; and Troilus now wounded one, now cast another from his horse. Wherever he went, it was thus: he was their death and for us the shield and life. As a result, on that day no one dared meet him while he had his bloody sword in hand. However, he can also be the friendliest man of high rank I ever saw in my life, when he so desires, and he can be the best of friends with those he thinks deserving." With these words Pandarus made as if to leave and said, "I must go."

"No, uncle, I am at fault," said Criseyde. "What is the matter that you are so soon tired, especially of women? Do you really wish to go? No, sit down, by God, I have some business, some wisdom to speak, before you go." Everyone who was with them and heard her words began to move away while they discussed their private matters.

When she had finished her account of her situation and management, Pandarus said, "Now it is time for me to go. But yet, I say get up and let us dance; cast your widow's clothes to the devil! Why do you wish so to disfigure yourself, since there is a good adventure in store for you."

"Ah, well remembered! For the love of God am I not to know what you mean by this?" she asked.

"No, this takes time," he then replied; "also I would certainly be grieved if I told you and you took it amiss. It is better that I hold my tongue than to speak a truth against your will. For niece, by the goddess Minerva, by Jupiter who

Book Two

makes the thunder ring, and by blessed Venus whom I serve, you are that woman living in the world without lovers, to my knowledge, whom I best love and am most loath to grieve; I think you know that well yourself."

"Certainly, uncle," she said; "thank you. I have always found you a friend. I am certainly indebted to no man so much as to you, and I have so little repaid you. But, by the grace of God, I shall to the extent of my wit never be guilty of offending you. If I have done so before now, I will amend it. But, for the love of God, I beg you, since you are the man I most love and trust, put aside your distant manner of speaking with me and tell me, your niece, whatever you wish."

At these words her uncle immediately kissed her and said, "Gladly, dear niece! Take well that which I shall now tell you." At this she cast her eyes down; Pandarus coughed a bit and continued, "Niece, look; you know that always some men choose to tell their tales with subtle art; yet despite all that, they mean the tale to have only one purpose. Now since the conclusion is the strength of every tale, and since this matter is so pleasing, why should I embellish or draw it out at length for you who are my faithful friend?" With these words he looked searchingly into her face and said, "Now good luck to a lovely woman!"

Then he thought, "If I make my story complicated or give a lengthy lecture, she will not like it at all, and will believe that I wish to trick her, for simple minds think all is trickery which they cannot fully understand; therefore, I'll find a way to make my story appealing for her"—and he looked closely at her, until she noticed that he stared at her, and said, "Lord,

Troilus and Criseyde

you stare hard at me! Haven't you seen me before now—what do you say?"

"Yes, yes," he replied; "and I'll see you more clearly before I go! But, on my word, I was just thinking whether you are lucky, for now men will clearly see your happiness. To everyone there is some good adventure in store at some time, if he can only accept it. But if he takes no notice of it when it appears, and purposely avoids it, then neither Fortune nor chance is to be blamed for his deception, which was actually caused by his own sloth and hesitancy; I think such a person is blameworthy.

"Fair niece, you have easily found your good adventure if you are wise enough to take it. For love of God and of me, grasp it at once lest your luck changes! Why should I make a longer story of this? Give me your hand, for, if you so desire, no one in the world will be so fortunate as you. Now, as I have told you before, since my intentions are good and I respect your honor and reputation as much as anyone in the world, by all the oaths I can swear, if you are angry at what I am going to tell you or if you think that I lie, I will never lay eyes on you again. Don't be afraid; don't tremble! Why should you? Don't change color from fright! For certainly the worst of this is over, and though my tale is new to you, trust that you will always find me dependable. If I thought it a thing not befitting you, I would not bring such matters to you."

"Now, good uncle," she said, "I pray you, for love of God, come on and tell me what it is! I am both afraid of what you will say and also longing mightily to know what it is! Whether it is good or bad, tell it; don't leave me longer in doubt."

Book Two

"I'll do it," said Pandarus. "Now listen, and I will tell you: My niece, the dear son of the king, the good, wise, worthy, lusty, generous and noble Troilus, who always bears himself well, so loves you that unless you help, he will die of it. See, that's all! Why should I say any more? Do what you like to cause him to live or die. But if you let him die, I shall die—you have my oath on it, niece; I will not deceive you—as surely as if I cut my throat with this knife."

With that, the tears burst from his eyes, and he said, "If you cause us both to die, though guiltless, you will have performed nobly! How will it help you to ruin us both? Alas, he who is my dear lord, that noble man, that brave, courteous knight, who desires nothing but your friendship, I see him dying: there he goes hastening with all his might straight towards death, if his fortune so wills it. Alas, that God gave you such beauty. If it happens that you are so cruel as to care nothing for his death—that noble, brave one, as you know—any more than for the death of a jokester or wretch,—if you are such a person, your beauty will not stretch to make amends for so cruel a deed. Meditation is good before a decision. Woe to the fair gem lacking in virtue; woe to the herb which furnishes no remedy! Woe to the beauty which is without pity; woe to the person who treads others underfoot! As for you, the full crop and the root of all beauty, if there is no pity within you, then on my word it is a shame that you live! Also, consider well that this is no trick; for I would rather that you, he, and I were hanged where all men could see us than that I should be his bawd! I am your uncle; I as well as you would be deserving of shame if I agreed to help him defile your honor. Now understand that I do not at all ask you to bind yourself

"If you let him die, I shall die"

to him through a promise, but only that you show him more attention and gaiety than you have in the past, so that at least his life will be saved: that is the sum total of our whole purpose. So help me God, I desire nothing else!

"You see that this request is only sensible, and that certainly it includes nothing unreasonable. To take the worst view, I suppose that you are afraid that people will wonder about his goings and comings to visit you. Against that I answer immediately that every person, unless he is a natural fool, will think Troilus is motivated by friendship only. Why, who will decide from seeing a man enter a temple that he eats the images within? Think also how well and wisely Troilus controls himself, so that he overlooks nothing and wins praise and thanks wherever he goes. In addition, he shall come here so seldom, what would it matter if all the city saw him? Such love between friends is customary throughout this city; conceal yourself always beneath that robe. As I hope wise God will be my salvation, it is best for you to do as I have said. But at least, good niece, in order to end his woe, let your haughtiness be a little sweetened so that you will not be to blame for his death."

Criseyde, having heard his story, thought, "I shall certainly probe him a bit." She said, "Now uncle, what would you suggest? What do you advise that I do in this matter?"

"That is well said," he replied. "Certainly, it is best that you love him in return for his love; since love for love is a sensible exchange. Think also how every hour old age destroys in each of you some part of beauty. Therefore, before age devours you, go love; for when you are old no man will desire you. Let this proverb be a guide for you: 'Too late aware,

Book Two

says Beauty when it has passed.' In the end, old age over-comes pride. It is the custom of the king's fool to cry out when he sees a woman who seems to bear herself too haughtily, 'May you and other proud ones live so long that crow's feet grow below your eyes; then may you have a mirror to gaze at, in which you may see your face each morning!' Niece, I can wish you no greater sorrow."

With these words he stopped and bowed his head; she at once burst into tears, saying, "Alas, woe! Why am I not dead? For faith has disappeared from all the world. Alas! What harm would strangers do to me when he whom I considered my best friend advises me to love when he should forbid me to do so? Alas! I would have been certain that if I had fallen in love with Hector, Achilles, or any man, you would have had no mercy or moderation for me, but would have constantly reproved me. Who, alas, can believe in this false world? What? Is this all my joy and my good fortune? Is this your advice? Is this my happy opportunity? Is this my full reward from your promise? Is all your artful story finished, alas? Was this your only purpose? O my lady Pallas! You take my part in this dreadful situation; for I am so amazed that I will die." With that she began to sigh sorrowfully.

"Ah! Can it be no better than that?" asked Pandarus. "By God, I shall come here no more this week if I am thus dis-trusted! I see clearly that you care little for us or our death. Alas! I am a woeful wretch! Do not worry about me as long as he can live. O cruel god, O unkind Mars, O three Furies of hell, I call upon you! Let me never go out of this house if I meant any harm or evil! But since I see that my lord must die, and I with him, I hereby confess myself and say that you, Criseyde, are wickedly causing both our deaths. And, by Neptune, god of the sea, since it suits you that I should die, from this day on I will not eat any bread until I can see my own heart's blood. For certainly, I wish to die as soon as Troilus."

Then he jumped up and hurried on his way, until she caught him by the coat. She was almost dead with fear, the most frightened person possible; also she had heard and seen Pandarus' serious purpose, and she found no faulty logic in his prayer. Thinking of the greater harm which might follow, she began to soften. Fearfully, she thought, "Misfortunes occur every day because of love, and in such situations men are naturally cruel and wicked. Alas, it would not be pleasant for this man to kill himself in my presence. I cannot imagine what people would say about it: I must proceed cautiously."

With a mournful sigh, she repeated three times, "Ah, Lord! What hard luck has come to me! For my position is now in jeopardy, and also my uncle's life is in the balance. But, nevertheless, with the help of God, I shall so handle matters that I shall guard my honor and also his life,"—and she stopped weeping. To Pandarus she said, "One should choose the lesser of two evils; thus I had rather be kind to Troilus, within the bounds of honor, than see my uncle lose his life. You say that there is nothing else in your request?"

"Certainly not, dear niece," answered Pandarus.

"Well," she said, " I will do my best. I shall force my heart against my liking, but I will not be more to him than a good friend. I cannot love a man against my will, but I shall manage to please him from day to day and still retain my honor. I would not have refused that at all, except that I was afraid in my imagination. But once the cause of sickness ceases, the

Book Two

malady disappears. Yet I hereby declare that if you ask more of me in this matter, though all the world at once turns against me, I will not have greater pity on him, even to save you both from death."

"I agree to that, on my word," said Pandarus. "But may I be sure that in the one thing you have here promised me you will keep faith with me?"

"Yes, without doubt, dear uncle."

"And that I shall have no reason to complain in the matter or to lecture you?" he asked.

"Why certainly not," she replied. "What need is there of further talk?"

Then they spoke of other, happy things until at last she said, "Good uncle, for the love of Him who made us both, tell me how you first learned of Troilus' woe. Does anyone know of it except you?"

"No," he answered.

"Can he speak well of love?" she asked. "I pray you tell me so that I shall better know how to conduct myself."

Then Pandarus began to smile a little and said, "On my word, I shall tell you. The other day, not a long time ago, Troilus and I spent almost half a day by a well in the palace garden to discuss a plan to bring grief to the Greeks. Soon after that we began to leap about and throw darts to and fro until at last he said that he was sleepy and lay down upon the grass. I wandered back and forth until, walking alone, I heard him groan piteously. I then crept up softly behind him and to tell the truth, as well as I can now recall it, he began pleading to Love, and said: 'Lord, have pity on my suffering, though I have been a rebel in the past; now, lord, I

Troilus and Criseyde

repent my sins! Oh god, who by just purveyance ordains the end of every individual, accept with favor my humble confession, and send me such penance as pleases you; but in your kindness be my guard against despair, which may separate my soul from you. For truly, lord, she who was dressed in black has with a glance of her eyes so sorely wounded me that I am touched to the bottom of my heart, by which I know that I must die. The worst of it is that I dare not declare my feelings, and the red coals grow hotter when men cover them with pale, dead ashes.'

"With these words he beat his head and began to mutter, I really don't know what. Then I went away quietly, quickly came back, and acted as if I had heard nothing. I stood by him and said, 'Wake up, you sleep too long! It seems that you are not troubled by love, since you sleep so heavily that no one can wake you. Whoever saw a man so unfeeling before now?' 'Yes, friend,' said Troilus, 'let your head ache for love, but let me live as best I can.' Though he was pale and wan with woe, he feigned as gay a manner then as if he were getting ready to lead the next dance.

"This went on until a few days ago. It happened that I came all alone into his room, and found him lying upon his bed. I never heard anyone groan so bitterly, and I had no idea what caused his trouble; for, as I approached, he suddenly stopped his complaint. This made me a bit suspicious; I moved nearer and found that he wept sorely. As I hope wise God will be my salvation, I never felt greater pity for anyone. I was scarcely able by tricks or by advice to keep him from death; even now I feel my heart weeping for him. God knows, never since I was born did I preach so earnestly to any man; never did I swear such oaths to any man before he told me who could be his doctor.

"But now do not ask me to rehearse for you all his words or to repeat all his woeful comments, for you would see me faint. I am determined to save his life; I am motivated by that reason only, and not to do you harm. So for the love of God who created us, be kind to him so that he and I may live! Now I have completely confessed myself to you, and since you know that my intention is pure, pay heed to my words, for I mean no evil. I pray to God that you will prosper from catching such a one without a net! If you are as wise as you are fair to look at, the ruby is set well in the ring. Never were there two so well met. May mighty God grant that we see the time when you are wholly his, as he is yours!"

"No, of that I spoke not at all," said she laughingly. "So help me God, you ruin everything!"

"Mercy, dear niece," he replied at once; "by Mars, the god with the steel helmet, whatever I said, I meant only well! Now don't be angry, my own dear niece."

"Well," she said, "let it all be forgiven."

With this he took his leave and went home. Lord, he felt proud and happy! Criseyde arose; she could not wait any longer, but at once went straight to her boudoir and sat down as still as a stone. Then she went up and down over every word Pandarus had said, as they came to her mind. The novelty of her situation dazed her mind somewhat; but when she had considered more fully, she found no danger or reason for fear. For it is possible that a man might love a woman to such an extent that his heart would break, while she need not return his love, unless she so desired.

Troilus and Criseyde

As Criseyde sat alone and thus speculated, a cry arose outside as a result of a skirmish on the battlefield. Men cried in the street, "See, Troilus has just now put to flight the Greek army!" At that, all her household began to shout, "Ah, let's go see! Open the gates wide! For he must pass through this street on his way to the palace; there is no other way from the gate of Dardanus, where the chain is lowered." Then Troilus and all his followers soon came riding by slowly in double ranks. Truly, this was his lucky day and, as everyone knows, nothing can be changed which is destined to happen.

Troilus, completely and richly armed except for his head, sat on his bay horse; the horse which he rode slowly along was wounded and bleeding. But Troilus presented such a knightly sight to those who saw him that he without doubt surpassed even Mars, who is god of battle. He was the picture of a true knight and man-at-arms, full of great strength. For he had the body and the will to do great things, as well as the courage. To see him dressed in his equipment—he seemed so vigorous, so young, and so agile—it was heavenly to look at him. His helmet was hacked in twenty places and hung down his back by a thread. His shield was smashed by swords and maces, and dangling from it one could find many an arrow, which had pierced horn, sinew, and hide.

Steadily the people shouted, 'Here comes our comforter, next to his brother, the first defender of Troy!" When he heard the people cheering him, he shyly turned a little red; it was delightful to see him modestly cast down his eyes. Criseyde carefully studied his face, and allowed it to sink so deeply into her heart that she asked herself, "Who gave me a drink?" Her thoughts caused her to turn red as she reminisced thus, "See,

Book Two

this is the man who my uncle swears must die unless I show him mercy and pity." At this thought, her embarrassment caused her to draw in her head quickly while he and all the people passed below. In her mind she went back and forth over his prowess, his rank, and also his renown, his wit, his form, and his courtesy. But she was pleased most highly because his distress was all on account of her. It seemed to her a pity to slay such a man, if his intentions were honorable.

Now some envious one might mock thus: "This was a sudden love; indeed, how could it be that she so easily loved Troilus at first sight?" But whoever says that, may he never prosper! Surely, everything must have a beginning before it can come to completion. I do not say that she suddenly gave him her love, but that she first began to be inclined to like him—and I have told you why; and after that his manhood and his suffering caused love to grow within her heart. Thus by degrees and good service he won her love, and not at all suddenly. Also blessed Venus sat well placed then in her seventh house of heaven. She was well disposed with helpful aspects to aid poor Troilus in his woe. To tell the truth, she was not an enemy to Troilus at his birth. God knows he more quickly made progress because of that!

Now let us leave Troilus riding along for a while and turn quickly to Criseyde, who hung her head low as she sat alone. She pondered what course she would decide to follow if her uncle would not stop forcing Troilus upon her. Lord, in her mind she argued so much about this matter which I have described to you, pondering back and forth what was best to do and what to avoid, that she twisted it into many folds. First her heart was warm, then it was cold; I shall write down a bit of that which my author decided to include about what she thought.

She thought it fortunate that she knew Troilus by sight and was also familiar with his courtesy. She said, "Although it will not do to grant him love, still because of his bravery it would be an honor to my situation—and good for his health—for me to play happily and honorably with such a lord. I know well that he is the son of my king; and since he takes such delight in the sight of me, if I were to flee from him completely, he might have me placed in such jeopardy that I would be in a worse plight than now. Would I be wise to bring hatred on myself unnecessarily when I might win favor? I know that the secret of everything lies in moderation. For though a man forbids drunkenness, I don't think he would demand that every creature be always without a drink. Also, since I know that Troilus' distress is on my account, I ought not despise him for it, because it is true that he means well.

"Further, for a long time I have known that he is virtuous and that he is not foolish. Certainly, people say that he is not a braggart; he is too wise to have so great a vice. Also, I shall never cherish him to such an extent that he can justly boast of it; he shall never bind me with such a clause. Now take this case: the worst would certainly be that people might think that he loves me. What dishonor would that be for me? Can I stop him from that? Why no, indeed! I know also—and each day I hear and see it—that men love women without their permission; and when they grow weary, let them stop! Then too, I realize that he is able to have the noblest woman of this city as his love, so long as she guards her honor. For, without doubt, he is the bravest of men except only Hector, who is the

Book Two

best. Yet his life now lies wholly within my care. But such is love, and also my destiny.

"It is no great wonder that he loves me, for, so help me God, I myself realize—although I would not want anyone to know it—that I am certainly one of the fairest and best in all the city of Troy; and people say so, if anyone cares to listen. What wonder is it that he takes pleasure in me? I am my own woman, financially comfortable in keeping with my position— thank God—reasonably young, and unattached in love, so that there is no jealousy or argument in which a husband can say to me 'Checkmate!' For husbands are either full of jealousy, or masterful, or they love novelty.

"What shall I do? To what end do I live now? Shall I not love if I so desire? Why, by the gods, I am not a nun. Even though I set my heart upon this knight, who is among the best, it will bring me no shame, so long as I guard my honor and reputation according to all the rules."

But just as the bright sun that shines in March often changes his face because the wind blows a cloud which spreads across the sun temporarily, so a cloudy thought ran through Criseyde's soul and covered over all her brighter thoughts; she almost fell from fright. That thought was this: "Alas, since I am free, should I now love and put my safety in jeopardy and my liberty in thrall? Alas, how dare I consider that folly? Can I not see clearly the fearful joy, the constraint, and the suffering of other folk. There is no one in love but that she has reason to complain. Love itself is surely the most stormy life there ever was, for there is in love always some mistrust or foolish quarrel, some cloud over the sun. We wretched women can do nothing when we are sad, except weep and sit and think. Our only revenge is to drink our own woe.

"Also, wicked tongues are so eager to speak harm of us, and men are so faithless, that as soon as their lust cools, love ceases, and away they go to a new love. But the harm done is done, whoever pities it. Though men at first torment themselves for love, a sharp beginning often comes to a feeble end. How many times has it been known that treason has been done to women in love! I cannot see the purpose of such love, or where it goes when it ends. There is no one who can tell, I think, where it goes; thus no one gets the best of it: what first was nothing ends as nothing. How busy I would have to be if I loved, to please those who mock and joke at love, and to cajole them into saying no evil of me! For even though there is no cause, it seems harmful to them that folk should please their friends; and who can halt every wicked tongue or the noise of bells which are ringing?"

After that, her thoughts began to clear, and she said, "He who undertakes nothing, gains nothing, be he willing or not"; and her heart trembled with another idea. Then her hopes slept and fear awoke. Now hot, now cold, thus caught between the two, she arose and went out for entertainment.

At once she went downstairs into the garden with her three nieces, and they took many a turn up and down. It was a joy to see the sport of Criseyde, Phlexippe, Tarbe, and Antigone; and a large group of her other women followed her all about the garden. This yard was large, with railed alleys shadowed well by leafy green branches; new benches were about, and all the paths were sanded. Criseyde walked arm in arm with her

nieces until Antigone began to sing a Trojan song so clearly
that it was heavenly to hear her voice.

ANTIGONE'S SONG

O Love, to whom I have been and shall
Be an humble subject, true in my intention,
As best I can, to you, lord, I give all
Control, forevermore, of my heart's desire,
For never did your grace send to anyone
So happy a cause as to me to lead my life
In complete joy and security, without fear.

You, blessed god, have so well placed me
In love that certainly all who bear life
Could not imagine how to better it;
For, lord, without jealousy or quarrel,
I love one who is the most attentive
To serve well, tireless and frank,
Who ever lived, and the least tainted with evil.

As the man who is the well of worthiness,
The ground of truth, the mirror of goodness,
Apollo in wit, the stone of steadfastness,
The root of strength, the origin and discoverer of joy,
Through whom all sorrow in me is killed—
Certainly, I love him best, as he does me;
Now may he have success, wheresoever he may go!

Troilus and Criseyde

Whom should I thank but you, god of Love,
For all this happiness in which I am bathed?
And thanks to you, lord, for the one I love!
This is the true life which I follow,
That overcomes all manner of vice and sin:
This causes me so to incline toward virtue
That day by day I amend my spirit.

And whoever says that to love is a vice,
Or servitude, though he find in it distress,
He is either jealous or foolish,
Or unable because of his scheming
To love; for such people, I think,
Defame Love, since they know nothing of him.
They speak out, but they never bend his bow!

Wherein is the sun the worse in its own nature
If a man, because of his weak eyesight,
Cannot endure to look at its brightness?
Or how is love the worse, if wretches cry out against it?
No success is worthwhile which entails no suffering.
And, therefore, he who has a head of glass
Must beware of stones cast at him in anger!

But I with all my heart and all my strength,
As I have said, will love until my death
My dear heart and my very own knight,
To whom my heart has grown so fast,
As his to me, that it shall endure forever.
Though at first I feared to start loving him,
Now I know well no danger lies therein.

Book Two

At that word she stopped her song, and Criseyde said, "Niece, who made that song which has such fine meaning?"

"Madam," immediately Antigone answered, "the best maiden of high rank in all the city of Troy; and she led her life in the greatest honor and happiness."

"Truly, it seems so from her song," remarked Criseyde, and began to sigh, asking, "Lord, is there such happiness among lovers that it makes them able to compose?"

"Yes, certainly," replied the fair Antigone, "for all the people who live or have lived cannot adequately describe the happiness of love. But do you think that every wretch knows the perfect bliss of love? Why certainly not! They think it is love if one is aroused. Away with them! They know nothing about it! People must ask saints if it is beautiful in heaven and fiends if it is foul in hell. Why?—for they can tell us."

Criseyde made no direct answer to this, but said, "Certainly, it will soon be night." But every word which had been spoken by Antigone was imprinted deep in her heart, and love frightened her less than it had at first. It crept into her heart, until she became almost converted.

The glory of the day, and the eye of heaven, the foe of night —I call the sun all this—began to sink rapidly in the west and to be hidden, since it had finished its daily course. White objects grew dim and gray for lack of light, and the stars appeared. Then Criseyde and her folk went inside together. When she was ready to go to bed, and everybody had left her room who was supposed to leave, she said that she was sleepy. Her women at once guided her to bed. When all was quiet, she lay still and thought over all these matters. I need not repeat all the details of her thoughts, for you are wise. A

Troilus and Criseyde

nightingale in a green cedar beside the wall of her room sang loudly in the shining moonlight—a love-song, perhaps, in his bird's fashion, which made her heart light and gay. She listened carefully to that song until at last she fell into a deep sleep. As she slept, she dreamed how an eagle with feathers white as bone set his long claws into her breast, tore out her heart, and put his heart into its place in her breast; by this deed she was not at all hurt or pained. Then he flew away, with heart left for heart.

Now let us leave her sleeping and take up our tale of Troilus, who has ridden to the palace from the skirmish of which I told, and sits now in his room waiting until two or three messengers whom he sent to seek Pandarus have finally found him and led him there. Pandarus soon came bounding in and said, "Who has been well beaten with swords and stone-sling today except Troilus, and who has caught himself a fever?" Then he continued jokingly, "Lord, how you sweat! But get up; let's have supper and go to bed."

Troilus answered, "We'll do as you like."

With all possible speed which accorded with good manners they hastened from supper to bed. And every other person left the room and went quickly on his way, wherever he wished. But Troilus, who felt his heart bleeding with woe, until he could hear some news, said, "Friend, shall I now weep or sing?"

Pandarus answered, "Lie still, let me sleep, and put on your night-cap. Your wishes are taken care of! Now choose whether you will sing or dance or leap! You must believe what I shall tell you briefly: Sir, my niece will do well by you and love you best; by God and on my word, lack of pursuit can come only from your laziness. For I have so conducted your case

53

Book Two

from day to day that this morning I won for you her friendly love, and also she has pledged her faith thereto. At any rate, a foot of your sorrow is removed!" Why should I make a longer sermon of this? You have already heard everything that Pandarus related to Troilus.

Just as flowers, shut in by the cold of night and bent low on their stalks, are refreshed by the bright sun and spread themselves in their natural manner in the row, so did Troilus cast up his eyes and say, "O dear Venus, may your power and your grace be praised here!" To Pandarus he held out both his hands, saying, "Lord, you can have all that I own! For I am well; my bonds are broken. So help me, wise God, one could not make me so happy by the gift of a thousand Troys one after the other. See, my heart swells so with joy that it will burst! But, lord, what shall I do? How can I live? When shall I next see my dear heart? How shall the long time be passed away until you visit her again for me? You may answer, 'Wait, wait,' but he who hangs by the neck truly waits in great discomfort because of his suffering."

"Go easy, now, for the love of Mars," said Pandarus, "for every thing has its proper time. Wait at least until the night is over, for as surely as you now lie here beside me, I shall be there at nine o'clock, as God is my witness. Therefore, you do as I say, or someone else can take over this responsibility. Indeed, God knows that I have always been ready to serve you, and until tonight I have done and shall do all I can to carry out your wishes. Do as I say now and act reasonably. If you will not, blame yourself for your troubles; your misfortunes are not my fault. I know well that you are a thousand times wiser than I, but, so help me God, if I were you I would now

Troilus and Criseyde

surely write her a letter in my own hand, in which I would tell
her that I fared badly and beg her pity. Now help yourself;
don't neglect it through laziness. And I shall go with it to her
myself.

"When you know that I am there, mount a horse immediately
in your best equipment and ride as if by chance in front of her
palace; you shall find us, if I can arrange it, sitting at some
window overlooking the street. And if you care to do so, you
can then salute us. Direct your greeting to me, but, on your
life, be wary and avoid tarrying too long—God protect us
from misfortune! When you have ridden on without showing
any loss of composure, she and I will speak about you somewhat, I think, so that your ears will burn after you have gone!

"You are wise enough to compose the letter well. I know you
will not write it too formally and fill it with difficult arguments.
Don't write too artfully or subtly; blot it a little with your
tears; and if you hit upon a good moving phrase, don't repeat
it too often. For though the best living harper had the finest
harp there ever was, and touched always the same string with
all his five fingers and played one tune steadily, no matter how
sharply his nails were pointed, everyone would be thoroughly
bored by his playing. Also, do not put together any dis-
cordant matters, such as mixing medical terms with love terms.
Hold always to the form of your subject and write that which
is fitting. For if a painter should depict a fish with ass's feet
and the head of an ape, it would not seem unified and would
be only a joke."

This advice pleased Troilus but, as a fearful lover, he said,
"Alas, dear brother Pandarus, I am certainly ashamed to write
lest in my innocence I say something amiss, or something

Book Two

which she would not receive sympathetically. Then nothing could prevent my death."

To this Pandarus answered, "If you wish, do as I say and let me go with it; by the Lord who made east and west, I hope to return quickly with an answer written in her own hand. But if you do not care to do so, let it go, and may hard luck come to him who helps you to success against your own wishes."

"Indeed, I agree," said Troilus. "Since you wish it, I shall get up and write. I earnestly pray blessed God to speed your trip and the letter which I shall write. And you, fair Minerva, give me skill to compose this letter."

Then he sat down and wrote in the following fashion. First, he called her his own lady, his heart's life, his joy, the physician for his sorrow, his bliss, and all the other names which lovers seek in such a situation. Then with humble words he began to recommend himself for her favor. To tell it all would require much space. Next, he meekly prayed her not to be angry, even though he in his folly made bold to write to her. He said that love caused him to do so, else he must die. Piteously he cried for mercy, and then said, laughing loudly, that he was of little worth, that he knew little, and that she must excuse his lack of skill caused by his great fear of her. He dwelt long upon his worthlessness, and then told her of his woe, which was endless. Last, he said that he would ever keep faith. Then he read the letter over and began to fold it. He bathed the ruby of his signet ring in his salty tears, and set it neatly and quickly upon the wax. He kissed the sealed letter a thousand times without stopping and said, "Letter, a happy chance is arranged for you: my lady shall see you!"

Troilus and Criseyde

Pandarus took the letter and, early next morning, went to his niece's palace. Upon arrival, he swore that it was after nine o'clock, and began to joke, saying, "Certainly, my heart is so lively even though it suffers that I can never sleep on a May morning. I have a jolly woe, a lusty sorrow."

Criseyde, when she heard her uncle, with a fearful heart yet desirous of hearing why he came, asked, "Now by your faith, dear uncle, what sort of winds have blown you here? Tell us about your jolly woe and your penance. How do you fare in love's dance?"

"By God," he answered, "I hop along always behind!"

She laughed until it seemed her heart would burst. Pandarus continued, "Be sure that you always find me fit for laughter. But listen, if you wish. Just now a stranger, a Greek spy, came into town, and he tells new things which I have come to tell you about. Let's go into the garden and you shall hear this long story in private."

With that they went together arm-in-arm down from the room into the garden. When they were far enough so that the sound of his voice could be heard by no one, he pulled out the letter and said to her, "See, he who is wholly yours freely and humbly recommends himself for your favor, and sends this letter here to you by me. Think about it when you have time, and make some fitting answer. Otherwise, so help me God, frankly he may not live long because of grief."

Fearfully, she then stood still and would not accept the letter. Her humble manner changed completely and she said, "For the love of God, bring me no billet concerning such matters. Also, dear uncle, I pray you have more regard for my position than for his lust! What more need I say? See now if

Book Two

this is reasonable; do not hesitate because of laziness or my feelings to speak the truth. Would it be in keeping with my position, by God and your word, to take the letter or to have pity on him to my own harm and reproach? Take it back, in the name of Him in whom you believe!"

Pandarus stared at her and said, "Now this is the greatest wonder I ever saw! Stop this foolish business! May I be smitten to death by thunder if, for the city which stands here, I would bring or carry a letter to you which would harm you! Why do you want to pretend so? But you act in every respect as if you care least what happens to him who wishes to serve you most, even whether he lives or dies. However, if I am deserving of any consideration, do not refuse this letter." Then he grabbed her and thrust the letter down her bosom, saying, "Now throw it away at once so that folks may look and stare at both of us."

Criseyde said, with a smile, "I can wait until they are gone. Uncle, I pray you prepare whatever answer you wish to carry back, for truly I will not write a letter."

"No?" asked Pandarus. "Well, then, I shall, if you will dictate it."

She laughed at that and said, "Let's go dine."

He began to mock himself, saying, "Niece, I suffer so greatly from love that I fast every other day." And then he brought forth his best jokes and made her laugh so hard with his foolishness that she thought she would die. When she came into the hall she said, "Now, uncle, we will dine at once," and called some of her women to her. Then she went straight into her room; one reason for her bustling around was that she wished because of fear to read the letter in private. She considered

Troilus and Criseyde

every word, line by line, and found no fault; it seemed to her that he wrote well. Then she put the letter up and went in to dinner.

Pandarus stood lost in thought and, before he was aware, she caught him by the hood and said, "You were caught before you knew it."

"I grant that," he replied. "Do what you like." Then they washed, sat themselves down, and ate. After dinner Pandarus very slyly began to edge over to the window nearest the street and said, "Niece, who has so decorated that house which stands opposite us?"

"Which house?" she asked, and moved near to look. She knew the house well, and told him whose it was. They fell into talk of unimportant matters, with both of them sitting in the window. When Pandarus saw his opportunity for gossip and noticed that her women had all moved away, he said, "Now, my niece, tell me: how did you like the letter that you received? Does he write well? On my word, I don't know."

At this she turned all rosy red, began to hum, and replied, "I think so."

"Repay him well," said Pandarus, "for the love of God; as a reward, I will sew together your reply." Then he held out his hands and kneeled down. "Now, good niece, no matter how small your letter, let me sew it together for you."

"Yes, I know so much about writing!" she said. "But I do not even know what to say to him."

"No, niece, don't claim that. At least thank him, I beg you, for his good will. Don't cause him to die," urged Pandarus. "Now, for love of me, dear niece, don't refuse my request this time!"

Book Two

"God grant all goes well," she said. "So help me God, this is the first letter that I ever wrote, yes, large or small." Then she went alone into a small room, the better to consider the matter. She loosed her heart somewhat from its prison of disdain, sat herself down, and began a letter, of which I plan to tell the main points as best I can. She thanked him for his good intentions toward her, but she would not give herself to him or bind herself in love. To please him and to comfort him she would always love him as a sister.

She sealed the letter, and went in to where Pandarus sat looking into the street. She sat down beside him on a stone of jasper with a gold-adorned cushion, and said, "So may almighty God help me, I never did anything more difficult than write this letter which you demanded of me." Then she gave it to him.

He thanked her, saying, "God knows, a good end often comes from things unwillingly started. And Criseyde, my niece, by God and yonder sun, Troilus ought to be glad that he has now won you with difficulty, for people say 'light impressions are easily put to flight.' But you have played the tyrant almost too long, and it was hard to engrave upon your heart. Now stop that, and don't behave in that fashion any longer, even though you wish to keep the appearance of reserve; but hasten to bring him joy. For you can be sure that tyranny practised too long causes hatred."

While they discussed this matter, Troilus appeared at the end of the street, riding slowly with ten comrades, and turned toward where they sat, as if on his way to the palace. Then Pandarus spied him and said, "Niece, look who comes riding

Troilus and Criseyde

by here! Don't run inside—I think he sees us—lest he think you are avoiding him."

"No, no," she said, and turned as red as a rose. Troilus then saluted her humbly with a frightened manner, and changed color often. Then he glanced gaily up to nod to Pandarus and passed on. God knows whether on that day he sat his horse well or made a fine appearance! God knows whether he seemed a manly knight! Why should I stop to tell of his finery? In brief, Criseyde, who saw all these things, liked the whole business—his person, equipment, appearance, attitude, attractive manner, and courtesy—so well that never since she was born had she felt such pity as for his distress. No matter how reluctant she had been earlier, I hope to God that now she has grasped a thorn which she shall not pull out within the next week. God send her more such thorns to pick at!

Pandarus, who stood right by her, felt the iron hot and began to strike. "Niece," he said, "I pray you heartily to answer that which I shall now ask you. Would the woman who was responsible for Troilus' death because she lacked pity have behaved well, since he is innocent?"

"No," she replied; "no, on my word!"

"So help me God," he said, "you speak the truth. You yourself feel that I do not lie. See, yonder he rides."

"Yes," she said, "so he does!"

"Well," said Pandarus, "as I have told you three times, put aside your silly modesty and your folly, and speak with him to ease his heart. Let not over-scrupulousness cause both of you harm." But this was too heavy a task for Pandarus. All things considered, this could not come about. Why? Because of modesty and also because it was too soon for Criseyde to grant Troilus so great a liberty. For her plain intention, as she said, was to love him without his knowing it, if she could, and to reward him with nothing but the sight of her.

But Pandarus thought, "It shall not be that way, if I can help it; this foolish opinion shall not be held by her for even two years." Why should I make a long sermon of this? For the time being, Pandarus must agree to her decision. When it was evening and they were in agreement, he rose and took his leave. He rushed homeward, and felt his heart dancing with joy. He found Troilus alone in bed, lying, as these lovers do, in a trance between hope and dark despair. As soon as he entered, Pandarus sang, as if to say, "I bring something good." Then he asked, "Who is so soon buried in bed?"

"It is I, friend," replied Troilus.

"Who, Troilus?" said Pandarus. "No, may the moon help me, you must get up and see a charm which was just sent to you and which can heal your woes if you bend all your efforts to it."

"Yes, through the power of God," said Troilus.

Pandarus gave him the letter and said, "Indeed, God has helped us! Take a light and examine all this writing."

How often Troilus' heart rejoiced and trembled as he read, when the words gave him reason for hope or fear. Finally, he took all that she had written for the best, since he now had something with which it seemed to him he could comfort his heart, even though she covered the words under a shield. He took notice of the more encouraging sections; thus, because of his hopes and Pandarus' promise, his greatest woe at least was overcome.

Troilus and Criseyde

But, as we ourselves may see every day, the more wood or coal, the greater the blaze; and just so, as hope increases for whatever it may be, desire also often grows. Or as an oak grows from a little sprout, so, as a result of this letter which she sent him, Troilus' burning desire began to grow. Therefore, I always say that day and night this Troilus, because of this new hope, began to wish for more than he formerly had, and he did all he could to make progress, according to Pandarus' suggestions, and to write her of his bitter sorrow. From day to day he did not allow his desire to cool at all, but sent a letter or message by Pandarus, and also did those other observances which are fitting for a lover in his situation. Then, depending on whether or not the dice turned in his favor, he was either happy or cried "Alas!" He held to the necessary stages of the affair and, in accordance with the answers he received, so were his days either sorrowful or glad.

But his recourse was always to Pandarus. Constantly, he piteously complained to him and asked him for advice and some help. Pandarus, who saw Troilus' insane suffering, actually almost died with sympathy, and busily studied with all his heart for some way to end Troilus' woe quickly. He said, "Lord, friend and dear brother, God knows that your disease causes me pain. Will you not stop this woebegone manner? On my word, before two days, with the help of God, I will so arrange matters that you shall go to a certain place in which you yourself may beg her for her favor. Certainly, I do not know whether you realize it, but those who are expert in love say that one of the things which results in the greatest progress is for a man to have an opportunity to plead in person and find a secure place to reveal his own woe. For it must arouse

Book Two

some pity in a good heart to see and hear the innocent in distress. Perhaps you think: 'Though Nature would cause her to begin to show a kind of pity upon my suffering, Disdain will say, "No, you shall never win me!" She so controls the spirit within her heart that though she bends, her roots still hold firm. What remedy for me is there in this?'

"On the other hand, think of this point: when the sturdy oak, upon which men have often hacked, receives the felling stroke, its great weight causes it to fall all at once like a rock or a millstone. For a thing with weight descends in a more rapid course than do light things. The reed which bows before every blast will easily rise when the wind ceases; but an oak will not do that when it falls. I need not preach to you at length. There can be no doubt that the longer men have been engaged in a great enterprise, the greater their rejoicing upon its completion. But, Troilus, you tell me, if you wish, a thing that I shall now ask you: which of your brothers do you love best in the very depths of your heart?"

"Certainly my brother Deiphebus," said Troilus.

"Well," said Pandarus, "within twenty-four hours, he shall comfort you, without knowing it himself. Now let me alone, to do as I wish." Then he went to Deiphebus, who had always been his lord and great friend, and who loved no one so well, except Troilus. Briefly Pandarus said, "I beg that you befriend a cause in which I am interested."

"Yes, certainly," said Deiphebus; "you know well that, as God is my witness, I will do as much for you as for any man, except my brother Troilus, whom I love best. But tell me what it is. For since the day I was born I never was and never will be more opposed to anything than to that which might cause you worry."

Pandarus thanked him and said, "See, sir, I have a lady in this town who is my niece and who is called Criseyde. Some men wish to oppress her and wrongfully to take over her possessions. Therefore, without any more talk, I beseech your lordship to be our friend."

Deiphebus asked, "Oh, is not this person to whom you refer as a stranger my friend, Criseyde?"

Pandarus replied, "Yes."

"Then," said Deiphebus, "there is hardly any need to say more, for you can be sure that I shall be her champion with spear and staff. I don't care if all her enemies heard it. But, tell me, you who know all the details of this matter, how can I best be of help?"

"Now, let's see," replied Pandarus; "if you, my dear lord, would do me the honor of inviting her to come visit you to-morrow to explain her difficulties, it would frighten her adversaries. And—if I dare ask more of you now and put you to so much trouble—having some of your brothers here when she comes would aid her cause; I know that she cannot fail to find support from you and from the acts of her other friends."

Deiphebus, whose natural love of honor and generosity led him to consent, answered, "It shall be done, and I can find even greater help than that, to my mind. What would you say if I sent for Helen to discuss this with her? I think it best, for she can influence Paris as she desires. There is no necessity for begging my brother Hector to be the friend of Criseyde, for I have heard him at one time or another speak so highly of her that he could say no finer things—such is her good for-

Book Two

tune with him. There is no need to beg his help; he will do whatever we ask. You yourself should also speak to Troilus on my behalf, and invite him to dine with us."

"Sir, all this shall be done," said Pandarus, and took his leave. He went nowhere else than to his niece's house, by the straightest path, and found that she had risen from dinner. He sat down and spoke as follows:

"By the true God, I have really been running! Look, niece, how I am sweating? I don't know whether you can thank me fittingly. Are you not aware that false Polyphetes is again about to bring complaints against you?"

"I? No," she said, and completely changed color. "What else is he doing to accuse me falsely and to wrong me? What shall I do, alas? I would fear nothing from him if it were not for Aeneas and Antenor, who are his friends in such matters. But, for the love of God, dear uncle, that doesn't matter; let him have everything he wants. Without those things, I have enough for us."

"No," said Pandarus, "it shall not be so. For I have just been to see Deiphebus, Hector and many other lords, and I have made them such enemies of Polyphetes that I'll swear he will never win in this business, no matter what he does or when he begins."

As they discussed what might best be done, Deiphebus courteously came himself to invite her to join him the next day at dinner. She could not refuse him, but politely accepted. He thanked her and went his way. When this was over, Pandarus rose immediately and took his way to Troilus, who waited still as a stone. To Troilus he told everything, word by word, about how he had deceived Deiphebus.

Troilus and Criseyde

Then he said, "Tomorrow is the time to bear yourself well, if you can, and all will be won. Now speak, now pray, now piteously complain. Don't stop because of foolish modesty, or fear, or laziness! Sometimes a man must tell his own suffering. Believe this and she will have pity on you: in truth you shall be saved by your sincerity. But I know well that you are now afraid, and I'll wager that I can tell you what causes this. You now think, 'How shall I do all this? For people will find out from my appearance that I am suffering for love of her; yet I had rather die of grief undiscovered.' Now do not think that, for it is very foolish. I have just discovered a way to conceal your appearance by a trick. You shall spend the night at Deiphebus' house, as if to drive away your malady by relaxation and sport—you do look sick, to tell the truth. Soon after your arrival there, go to bed, saying that you can stay up no longer, and lie there awaiting what will happen. Say that you are habitually seized by fever at that hour, and that it lasts until the next morning. And let me see how well you can pretend, for actually he who grieves is really sick. Go now; farewell. As Venus is my witness, if you carry out this plan, I hope that there Criseyde will give you her full favor."

Troilus replied, "Certainly, there is no need to advise me how to feign sickness, for I am so truly ill that I nearly die with the pain."

"In that case," said Pandarus, "you shall complain better and have less need to pretend, for people consider a man feverish when they see him sweating. Be sure that you keep carefully to the arrangements, and I shall surely drive this deer into range of your bow." Then he took his leave quietly, and Troilus went happily to the palace. He was never so

Book Two

joyful in his life, and gave his full consent to Pandarus' plan. That night he went to the house of Deiphebus.

What need is there to tell you all the hospitality that Deiphebus showed his brother, or of Troilus' feigned fever or his sickly look, or of how he was loaded with cover when he was taken to bed, and how the people tried to cheer him up? All was in vain; Troilus continued steadfastly with the plan which you have just heard Pandarus expound. But it is certain that before Troilus went to bed Deiphebus had begged him to be a friend and helper to Criseyde. God knows that he immediately agreed to be her staunch friend to the best of his ability. In fact, it was as necessary to ask that of him as to ask a crazy man to run.

Morning came and the time for dinner approached. Helen had planned to be with Deiphebus, whom she did not wish to disappoint, by ten o'clock. Meekly, as his sister, she came to dine. Only God and Pandarus knew what all this meant. Criseyde came also, completely innocent, with Antigone and her sister Tarbe. But it is best for us to avoid prolixity now, and go rapidly without wasted words to the point. All these folk were assembled there—we can skip their greetings.

Deiphebus did them great honor and fed them well with all the things which might please them. But his constant refrain was "Alas, my good brother Troilus still lies sick," and with that he sighed. Then he did his best to entertain the company and make them happy. Helen also complained so sincerely of Troilus' illness that it was pitiful to hear, and all of a sudden everybody became a doctor. They said, "Here is the way to cure sickness;" and "I shall teach you about this charm." Only one person who sat there did not desire to teach cures; she

Troilus and Criseyde

thought, "I could be the best doctor for him." After sympathizing with him, they praised him; as people usually do when one person starts to praise a man others increase the praise a thousandfold higher than the sun: "He is this, and he can do that which few lords can do." Also, Pandarus did not forget to confirm the points which they claimed.

Criseyde heard all these things clearly enough, and took note of every word. As a result, despite her sober manner, her heart laughed. For who could fail to glorify her for being able to cause such a knight to live or die? But I skip over all this, lest you grow bored, for everything I tell is toward one end. The time arrived for them to rise from dinner, and they did so properly. For a short time they spoke of this and that, but Pandarus soon broke into the conversation and said to Deiphebus, "Would you care to begin, as I requested you, the discussion here of Criseyde's difficulties?" Helen, who was holding Criseyde by the hand, spoke first, saying, "Let us do so rapidly." She looked fondly at Criseyde and continued, "May Jove never permit that man to prosper who does you harm; may he soon die. And may I have sorrow if I fail to do everything that I can, with the help of all honest folk, to make him regret it."

Deiphebus said to Pandarus, "Describe your niece's situation, for you know it best."

"My lords and ladies, here is the situation," said Pandarus. "Why should I keep you a long time?" For them he rang out the story like a bell, and painted her enemy named Polyphetes in such a hateful manner that one wished to spit on him. Each one spoke out more vigorously against this than the other, and they all cursed Polyphetes. "Let such a man be hanged, even

Book Two

if he were my brother! And so he shall; nothing shall prevent it!" Why should I continue longer? Briefly, all together they promised her that they would help her in any way they could.

Helen then said, "Pandarus, does my lord and brother Hector know anything of this? Or does Troilus know of it?"

"Yes," said Pandarus; "but do you want to hear my suggestion? It seems to me that since Troilus is here it would be good, if you all agree, for Criseyde to tell him about it herself before she leaves. For he will then take her grief more to heart, because she is a lady. If you agree, I shall just peep in and let you know at once whether he sleeps or wishes to hear anything of this matter."

Then he rushed in and whispered into Troilus' ear, "God take your soul; I am bringing your pillow!" Troilus smiled, while Pandarus returned at once to Helen and Deiphebus without more discussion and reported, "If there is no lingering and no crowd, he wants you to bring my lady Criseyde in to him. As long as he is able, he will listen to her. But you know the room is very small and a few people can easily heat it up. Now you decide—for I do not wish to be blamed for bringing in a crowd which will hurt him or make him sicker, not for my right arm—whether it is better for her to wait until another time; decide now, you who know what should be done. It seems to me, as far as I can tell, that it would be best if no one went in except you two, except possibly for me also, for I can in a moment retell her situation better than she. After that she may ask him once briefly to be a good lord, and then take her leave. This could not disturb him very much. Also, since she is a stranger, she would discomfort him, whereas you two would not. Then, too, he wants to tell you both about another

70

Troilus and Criseyde

matter—I know it well—which is secret and concerns the city's safety."

Helen and Deiphebus, knowing nothing of Pandarus' purpose, went in to Troilus without further discussion. Helen, in her pleasant and gentle way, greeted him and, joking in feminine fashion, said, "Certainly you must soon get up! Now get well, brother, I pray you!" She placed her arm over his shoulder and did her best to comfort him. She tried hard to cheer him up. Then she said, " We, Deiphebus and I, beseech you, my dear brother, for the love of God—and so does Pandarus also—willingly to be a good lord and friend to Criseyde, who is certainly being wronged, as Pandarus here knows well; he can explain her situation better than I."

Then Pandarus once more sweetened his tongue and rapidly retold her case. When it was over, Troilus at once said, "As soon as I can walk I shall gladly be one of those supporting her cause; God has my promise."

Queen Helen said, "Bless you for that!"

Pandarus then asked, "Is it your will that she take her leave of you before she goes?"

"Oh, God forbid otherwise," said Troilus, "if she would be so kind as to do so." Then he continued, "You two, Deiphebus and my dear sister, I wish to speak to you of one matter, to have your best advice—"; and it so happened that he found at his bedside the copy of a treatise and a letter which Hector had asked him to read, concerning whether a certain man deserved to die, I don't know who. But Troilus very seriously begged them to consider the matter at once. Deiphebus earnestly unfolded the letter, and so did Helen; then, wandering out of the room and down a stairway into a green arbor,

Book Two

they examined it carefully. They studied and discussed this matter in detail between them for the better part of an hour.

Now let them read, and we shall turn at once to Pandarus who quickly determined that all went well. Then he rushed out into the large room and said, "God save all this company! Come, my niece, my lady Queen Helen waits for you with my two lords. Rise and bring your niece Antigone, or whomever you wish, with you. No, that doesn't matter; the less crowd, the better. Come on alone with me and see that you humbly thank all three of them. And when you see your chance, take your leave of them lest we keep Troilus too long from his rest."

All innocent of Pandarus' intention, Criseyde said, "Let us go, uncle dear," and arm in arm she went in with him, considering well her manner and her words. Pandarus said seriously, "I ask all you people, for the love of God, to stay here and not make such noise. Remember who is within this room and in what state one of them is, God help him."

As they entered, Pandarus whispered to Criseyde, "Begin gently, niece, I urge and command you, on behalf of Him who sent a soul to each of us. Do not for the value of two crowns kill this man who suffers so because of you! Fie on the devil! Think what kind of man he is and in what plight he stands. Come on at once! Think that time wasted is but lost; you will both say that when you are united. Secondly, no one yet suspects you two. Come on now, if you can! While folk are blinded, time is gained. From chattering, pursuit, and delays, people can easily guess what is happening; and later, though you wish for happy days, you dare not grasp them. Why? Because this woman or that one spoke such a word, and this man or that one looked so! For fear of losing time, I dare not

72

Troilus and Criseyde

argue with you any longer. Therefore, come on and bring him back to health!"

But now, you lovers who are here, wasn't Troilus in a terrible state? He could hear their whispering from where he lay, and thought, "O Lord, the decision as to whether I shall die or find comfort is now being settled!" And this was the first time that he would beg her love in person. O mighty God, what should he say?

HERE ENDS BOOK II

Here Begins Book III

blessed planet, Venus, whose dear beams adorn all the third sphere of heaven! O beloved of the sun; O dear daughter of Jove; O kind, happy giver of love's joy, ever ready to enter gentle hearts! O true cause of well-being and gladness, praised be your power and goodness! Your might is felt in heaven and hell, on earth and in the salty sea, if I understand clearly. Man, bird, beast, fish, herb, and green tree at times feel your eternal influence. God loves and will not deny love; in this world no living creature is worthwhile or can endure without love. You first brought Jove to those happy acts through which all things live and exist, and made him amorous of mortal beings; as you desired, you always gave him comfort or trouble in love. In a thousand forms you sent him down to earth for love, and he possessed whom you wished. You appeased the anger of fierce Mars and, as you wish, you can ennoble hearts.

Always those whom you wish to set afire fear shame and leave vice; you make them courteous, lusty, and kind. To high or low, according to his merit, your power sends the joys he experiences. You hold realm and household in unity; you are also the true cause of friendship. You know all those hidden qualities of things at which folks so wonder, when they cannot understand how it may be that she loves him or why he loves her, or why this fish and not that comes into the

Troilus and Criseyde

net. You have established a law for folk throughout the universe—I know this from those who are lovers—and whoever strives against you comes off worse. Now, bright lady, in your kindness and in reverence of those who serve you, whose cleric I am, teach me how to show some of the joy which is felt by those in your service. Inspire sentiment in my naked heart, and permit me to show some of your sweetness.

Calliope, may your voice also be present now when it is needed; do you not see my distress, how I, in praise of Venus, must straightway tell the joy of Troilus? May God bring that happiness to him who needs it!

Meanwhile, Troilus lay rehearsing his lesson in this manner: "My faith," he thought, "I shall say this and that; thus shall I plead with my dear lady. That word is good, and I shall act this way; this I must by no means forget." God grant that he can act as well as he imagines! Lord, his heart began to tremble and his breath to come rapidly when he heard Criseyde approach!

Then Pandarus, who led her by the cloak, came in, raised the bed-curtain, and said, "God cure all the sick! Look who has come to visit you; see, here is she who is to blame for your death"; and he seemed almost ready to weep.

"Ha, ha," said Troilus ruefully. "You know, mighty God, what causes my woe! Who is there? I can't see clearly."

"Sir," said Criseyde, "it is Pandarus and I."

"Yes, sweetheart?" said Troilus. "Alas, I cannot rise to kneel and do you honor." He raised himself upright, but she immediately placed both hands gently upon him.

"Oh, for the love of God, do not do that for me," she said. "What does this mean? Sir, I came to you for two causes:

Book Three

first, to thank you; and also I wish to ask you to continue your friendship."

Troilus, upon hearing his lady beg his friendship, felt himself between life and death, and for shyness he could not speak a word, even if his head were to be cut off. But, Lord, he turned red suddenly, and his lesson, which he thought he had memorized for her, ran from his mind.

Criseyde noticed all this well, for she was wise, and she loved him no less because he was not glib, or forward, or so bold as to sing a mass for a fool. When his embarrassment had passed somewhat he spoke his piece, which I shall tell you as well as my words can reproduce what old books teach. In a changed voice that shook with fear, and in an humble manner, now blushing, now pale, with downcast eyes and modest look he spoke to his dear lady Criseyde. The first word he uttered, twice-repeated, was, "Mercy, mercy, sweetheart!" Then he stopped for a while; the next words he could bring out were, "God knows that, in so far as I have the skill, I have always been yours, and so shall I be until I, woeful one, am buried! Though I dare not and cannot plead with you, I suffer no less pain. This much I can now bring forth, O perfect woman, and if it displeases you, I shall at once avenge it upon my own life to comfort your heart, if by my death I can appease your wrath. But since you have heard me speak some of my feelings, I do not care how soon I die."

To look upon his manly sorrow would have softened a heart of stone. Pandarus wept as if he would turn to water. Time after time he poked his niece and said, "True hearts are woebegone! For the love of God, put an end to this thing, or else kill us both before you go."

Troilus and Criseyde

"I? What?" asked Criseyde. "By God and on my word, I do not know what you want me to say."

"I? What?" mocked Pandarus. "That you have pity on him, for the love of God, and not cause him to die."

"Then I wish to ask him to tell me now the end of his intentions. I never did understand just what he meant," said Criseyde.

"What I mean, dear sweetheart?" cried Troilus. "O noble, blossoming, generous one, I ask that sometimes you look at me in a friendly fashion with the beams from your bright eyes, and that you consent that I might be the man who, without any hint of vice, could serve you faithfully as my own lady and chief refuge, with all my wit and diligence. I would accept death, in accordance with your desires, as a comfort equal to my guilt if I so transgressed as to break down your defenses. I ask that you condescend to do me the honor of commanding anything of me at any hour, and to you I will be true, humble, faithful, secret, and patient in suffering; and evermore, I will desire to serve you and to be steadily diligent. I will receive with good heart all your decisions, no matter how they pain me,—see, that is what I mean, my own sweetheart."

Pandarus said, "See, here is a reasonable request and a hard one for a lady to deny! Now my niece, if I were a god you would die as soon as the birthday feast of Jove, for you heard well that this man desires nothing but that which does honor to you; yet you see him dying and are loath to allow him to serve you."

At that she cast her eyes on Troilus gently and pleasantly; she meditated and was not in any hurry to speak. Gently she said to him, "Within the bounds of my honor, and in the man-

Book Three

ner Troilus just described, I will gladly receive him fully into my service, beseeching him for the love of God that he will mean well towards me, in accord with the truth and courtesy which I intend, and will always guard my honor with his wit and efforts. If in the future I can make him happy, certainly, I shall do so without pretense. Now be cured; plead no longer! Nevertheless, of this I warn you: though you are certainly the son of a king, you shall no more have sovereignty over me in love than is just. Nor will it help to be angry if you do amiss. While you serve me, I shall cherish you in accordance with your deserts. Thus, dear heart and my knight, be happy and get back your health. I shall truly with all my ability turn your bitterness to sweetness. If I am she who can make you happy, you shall receive joy for every woe." Then she took him in her arms and kissed him.

Pandarus fell to his knees, cast his eyes up to heaven, raised his hands, and said, "Immortal god, who cannot die—I mean Cupid—you must glorify this. And Venus, you must make melody! It seems to me that because of this miracle I hear every bell in the city ringing without being pulled. But wait! No more of this matter now, for those two who have read Hector's letter will soon come up. I hear them now. But I serve notice on you for one, Criseyde, and you Troilus for the other, that when you can walk again you should be ready to come to my house when invited, for I plan to have you there to comfort your hearts fully. Let's see then which of you will win the prize in speaking of love! You will have leisure there to talk"—and he laughed at this.

Troilus asked, "How long must I wait before this is done?"

Troilus and Criseyde

Pandarus replied, "When you can get up, it shall be just as I promised."

At that Helen and Deiphebus came up to the head of the stairs, and, Lord, Troilus began to groan loudly in order to deceive his brother and sister. Pandarus said, "It is time for us to go. Niece, take your leave of all three; come out with me and let them speak together."

She took her leave very properly, as she knew well how to do, and they did full reverence to her and spoke very kindly of her after she left, praising her excellence, her tact, and her wit, and commending her manners; it was a joy to hear.

Now let Criseyde return to her own palace, and we shall turn again to Troilus who rapidly read the letter Deiphebus had examined in the garden. He wished to be rid of Helen and Deiphebus, and said he wished to sleep, to rest after the talking. Helen kissed him and quickly took her leave; Deiphebus did the same, and everyone went home. Pandarus, as fast as he could run, came straight as a line to Troilus and lay all that happy night on a pallet beside his bed to talk merrily. It was well that they were together. When everyone had left except the two of them and the doors were shut tight, Pandarus rose to talk without interruption and sat on the side of Troilus' bed. He began to speak soberly to Troilus, as I shall tell you!

"My best-loved lord and dear brother, God and you know that it grieved me sorely when I saw you languishing so for love, because of which your woe grew steadily greater. Ever since then I have bent all my efforts and abilities toward bringing you out of distress to joy. I have brought things to such a situation that you know that through me you are now likely to fare well. I do not say this as a boast. Do you know why?

Book Three

Because I began on your account to play a game—it is a disgrace to say it—which I shall never play again for another man, even though he were my brother a thousandfold. That is to say, for you I have become, between joking and seriousness, such a man as makes women come to men. Though I do not mention the word, you know what I mean. For you I have made my niece, so innocent of vice, trust your courtesy so fully that you shall fulfill all your desires. But I take God who knows all as my witness that I did not do this for covetousness, but only to lighten that distress because of which you almost died, it seemed to me.

"Good brother, act now as you should, for the love of God, and keep her from blame, since you are wise, and always guard her reputation. For you know well that her name now is hallowed here among the people; I can swear that the man is yet unborn who ever knew of her doing amiss. But woe to me, who brought all this about, when I think that she is my niece and that I am at the same time her uncle and a traitor to her! If it were known that through my deception I had put my niece in this situation to satisfy your desires and to be wholly yours, why, all the world would cry out against it and say that in this instance I performed the greatest treachery ever done, whereby she is ruined and you have profited not at all. Therefore, before I go further, I again beseech and urge you that secrecy accompany us in this matter; that is to say, you must never expose us. Do not be angry because I so often ask you to keep secret such an important matter, for my request is reasonable, you know well. Think what woe has come about in the past, as one may read, because of boasting, and what misfortune there still is in the world

She took her leave very properly, as she knew well how to do . . .

Troilus and Criseyde

from day to day as a result of the same wicked deed. For that reason the wise clerics who are dead left a proverb to guide us in youth: 'The highest virtue is to hold your tongue.'

"Were it not that I now wish to be brief, I could tell you almost a thousand ancient stories of women lost through false and foolish boasting. You yourself know many proverbs against the vice of foolish chattering, even if men told the truth as often as they lie. O tongue, alas, so often in the past you have made many a fair lady cry 'Woe was the day that I was born!' You have renewed many a young girl's sorrow; yet, for the most part, all is false which men spread by boasting, if it were brought to the proof. By nature no braggart can be trusted. A braggart and a liar are one; for example, if a woman grants me her love and says that she desires no other man, and though I have sworn to keep it secret I afterwards go tell it to two or three people, certainly I am a braggart at least and a liar in breaking my oath. Now see if that kind of folk is not to be blamed—what shall I call them—those who boast about women and even name them, though the women never promised anything nor knew the braggarts better than my old hat! As God may send me health, it is no wonder that women are afraid to deal with us men. I do not say this because I distrust you or any wise man, but because of stupid fools and the evil which is now in the world, as much because of folly as of malice. For I know well that no woman fears this vice in a wise man, if only she is well advised. Wise men are punished for the evil done by fools.

"But now to my point: bear all this which I have said in mind, dear brother, and keep this affair secret. Now cheer up, for in your time of need you will find me faithful. If God permits,

Book Three

I shall so arrange this matter that it will satisfy you and be just as you wish it. For I know that you mean well, indeed; therefore, I am willing to undertake this whole matter. You know also what your lady granted you; and the day is set to draw up the contracts. Good night, now, I can remain awake no longer. Pray for me, since you are in bliss, so that God will send me death or some relief."

Who could tell even half the joy or gladness Troilus felt in his soul upon hearing Pandarus' promise? His old woe, which had made his heart suffer, began to decrease and melt into joy. All his deep sighs departed at once; he felt them no more. Just as the woods and fields which have been dry and dead throughout the winter redecorate themselves in green when May arrives, the time when every lusty person becomes playful, so it truly was that Troilus' heart filled with such happiness that there was never a more joyful man in Troy.

He looked at Pandarus in a serious and friendly way and said, "Friend, last April, as you know if you recall it, you found me nearly dead because of grief, and you did all you could to learn from me the cause of my distress. You remember how long I hesitated to tell even you, the man I most trust; and I knew well there was no danger in telling you. Show me then, if you wish, since I was so loath for you to know it, how I could dare, trembling even now when no one can hear us, reveal this matter to others? Nevertheless, by the God who governs all this world as He desires, I swear that I would rather die and come to my end, it seems to me, surrounded by wretchedness, filth, and vermin as a prisoner of cruel King Agamemnon. May Achilles pierce my heart with his spear, though my life were as eternal as it is mortal, if I lie; or if late or soon

82

Troilus and Criseyde

I would or dared or could reveal this affair for all the riches
God made under the sun. In all the temples of this city, I will
swear this to you tomorrow by all the gods, if you wish to hear
it. I know that you have done so much for me that I can never
deserve it, though I might one day die a thousand deaths for
you. I can say no more than that I shall serve you as your
slave wherever you go, forever until I die.

"But I beseech you here with all my heart never to think
me so foolish as to reveal this matter. It seemed to me from
your words that you thought that I consider this a bawdery
which you are doing for me out of friendship. I am not insane,
even if I am ignorant! I know well that it is indeed not so!
A man who arranges such affairs for gold or riches, call him
whatever you like; and this which you do, call it courtesy,
compassion, friendship, and trust. Make this distinction, for
it is widely known, as I have learned, that there is a difference
between things which look alike. In order that you shall
believe that I do not think or consider this service which you
do me a shame or a joke, take as your own my fair sister
Polyxena, Cassandra, Helen, or any of the lot, no matter how
beautiful or well formed she is; tell me which one of all these
you desire, and then let me alone. Since you have done me
the service to save my life, without hope of reward, so for the
love of God, bring it to a suitable end, for now there is the
greatest need. Without doubt, in spite of high and low, I will
always do your bidding. Now good night; let's both go to
sleep."

Thus each of them was so well pleased with the other that
there was no way in the world for the situation to be improved.
In the morning when they were dressed, each set out to attend

Book Three

to his own affairs. But Troilus, though he burned like fire with the hope of pleasure, remembered to maintain his self-control. In a manly fashion he restrained each rash deed and unbridled look, so that all who lived could not really know from his words or manner what he thought in connection with this affair. So well could he dissemble that he was as far as a cloud from everyone's understanding.

During all this time, here was Troilus' life: by day with all his power he was in the high service of Mars—that is to say, engaged as a knight at arms; through the long night he lay for the most part thinking how he might best serve his lady in order to deserve her thanks. I shall not swear that though he rested comfortably he was not to some extent disturbed in mind, or that he seldom twisted on his pillow, desiring that which he lacked. In such a situation, there is no man, for aught I know, who is any more pleased than was Troilus; at least I consider that a possibility.

Now, to continue the story—it is certain that during this period, as it is written in the histories, Troilus saw his lady sometimes, and also she spoke with him when she dared and desired to do so. By mutual consent, they both carefully discussed how they dared proceed in this matter. Their conversations, however, were so brief and were carried out in such fear of someone's guessing or imagining what was in progress, or listening to their talk, that they wished for nothing in the world so much as that Cupid would grant them the chance to finish their discussion. But in the little that they did talk or decide together, he was so wisely aware, that it seemed to her he knew what she thought without words, so that there was no need to bid him or forbid him to do anything. As a result,

Troilus and Criseyde

she thought that love, though it had arrived late, had opened
he gates of all joy for her.

To conclude this point briefly: he was so careful in his words
and deeds that he stood high in his lady's favor, and she thanked
God twenty thousand times without pause that she had met
Troilus. He knew so well how to control himself in such
service that all the world could not arrange it better. She
found him so discreet, secret, and obedient in everything that
he seemed to her a wall of steel, shielding her from every displeasure. Because of his self-control and wisdom she was no
longer afraid—I mean not so much as she might have been in
the circumstances. Meanwhile, Pandarus, to keep the fire
burning steadily, was constantly diligent and eager. His whole
purpose was to bring comfort to his friend. He pushed con-
tinually onward, and was sent back and forth. He carried letters when Troilus was absent; without doubt, there never was
a man who conducted himself better in helping his friend.

Now, perhaps, some listener is waiting for me to rehearse
every word, sound, look, or action of Troilus towards his lady
during this period. I think it would be a boring thing to hear
a description of all the words or looks of any man who was
in such a situation. Truly, I think that neither I nor anyone
present has heard that done in any story before. Even if I
wished to do so, I certainly could not, for there were some
letters which passed between them that were almost half as
long as this book—so says my author, and he decided not to
reproduce them. How then could I write a single line of them?

But to the main point: I say that these two, Criseyde and
Troilus, stood in complete peace and accord during this pleasant interval, as I have indicated,—except that they could not

Book Three

meet often, or have time to finish their conversations. Then
it happened, as I shall tell you, that Pandarus did all he could
towards that end which I shall mention; namely, one night to
bring Troilus and his fair niece together at his house, where
they might discuss at leisure all this important matter concerning their love. For with great deliberation he had planned
and executed all the details for this meeting, omitting nothing
because of expense or trouble. If they cared to come, they
would find nothing lacking. He knew that it was wholly im-
possible for them to be in any way spied on there. Without
doubt, the air was clear of every magpie and every spoil-sport
Now all was well, for all the world was blind to this affair,
both foreigners and natives. The timber was all set for the
framework; we lack nothing but the knowledge of the definite
hour when she will come.

Troilus, who knew fully all these preparations, and waited
impatiently for the day, had also made careful arrangements.
He prepared his reason and his clothing for going away so
that if he were missed by day or night while he was engaged
in this matter, he could say that he had gone to do his sacrifice
and had had to watch alone in such and such a temple in order
to receive an answer from Apollo; and in order first to see the
holy laurel tremble before Apollo told him from the tree when
next the Greeks would be put to flight—in this let no man
hinder him, God forbid, but rather pray for Apollo's help.

Now little was left to be done. Soon after the change of
the moon, when the world was dark for a night or two, it looked
as if there would be rain, and Pandarus went one morning
straight to his niece. You have already heard his purpose.
When he arrived, he at once began to joke, as was his custom,

86

Troilus and Criseyde

and to poke fun at himself. Finally, he swore by this and that, and told her that she could no longer avoid him or continue to make him run after her, but that certainly she must willingly come to supper at his house that evening.

She laughed at this and quickly began to make excuses, saying, "It is raining; see, how can I walk out?"

"Put aside such fanciful talk," he replied. "This must be done! You can get there quickly."

So at last they came to an agreement; otherwise, he whispered in her ear, he would never come to visit her again. Soon afterwards, she began to whisper to him and asked him if Troilus would be there. He swore not, for Troilus was out of town, and said, "Niece, suppose that he were. You need not therefore be afraid; I would rather die a thousand times than have people see him there with you."

My author did not care to reveal fully what she thought when he said that Troilus had gone out of town: whether she thought Pandarus spoke the truth or not. But without hesitation she agreed to go with him to dinner, since he wished that, and as his niece she owed him obedience. Nevertheless, though she had no fear in going to his house, she begged him to beware of the gossip of stupid people who imagined things which never happened, and to be careful of whom he invited there. Then she said, "Uncle, since I must trust you, see that all is well; now do whatever you wish."

Pandarus swore by sticks and by stones, and by the gods who dwell in heaven, that he would be careful and that he would rather his soul and his body should be with King Pluto as deep in hell as Tantalus, than be negligent! What more should I say? When all was well, he rose and took his leave.

Book Three

When it was evening Criseyde came to supper with certain of her own men in attendance, with her niece Antigone, and with nine or ten of her other women. But now who do you think was happy except Troilus? He stood by a little window in a closet, from which he could see her arrival. Since the previous midnight he had been cooped up in this small closet, unknown to everyone except Pandarus. But to the point: when Criseyde arrived amid all the happy and friendly greetings, her uncle at once took her in his arms, and later at the proper time they comfortably sat down all together for supper. God knows, there was no dainty lacking! After supper they rose, at ease and with gay and friendly spirits; happy was the man who managed best to please Criseyde, or to make her laugh. Pandarus sang; Criseyde joked; then he told a tale about Wade. But at last, as all things must have an end, she took her leave and must depart for home.

But O Fortune, executrix of destiny; O influences of the high heaven! The truth is that under God you are our supervisors, though the causes are hidden from us beasts. I mean here that Criseyde started homeward, but the will of the gods was all against her leaving. Therefore, she had to remain. The crescent moon with her pale horns, Saturn, and Jove were all met in Cancer; as a result such a rain began to fall from heaven that every woman who was there felt great fear of the smoky rain. Pandarus laughed at that and said, "This is a fine time for a lady to leave! But good niece, if I can ever please you in any way, I pray you to do me the pleasure of spending the whole night in my house; indeed, this is your own house. On my word—and I do not say it jokingly—for you to go now would shame me."

Troilus and Criseyde

Criseyde, who well realized the truth of his statement, listened to his request, and since it rained so that everything was flooded, she thought, "It is as good a bargain to agree to remain here willingly and in a friendly fashion, for which I shall receive thanks, as to grumble about it and then stay. It is certain that I cannot go home." She said "Dear uncle, I shall stay; since you wish it, it is reasonable to have it so. I am quite happy to stay here with you; I only joked when I said I would leave."

"Thank you, indeed, niece," he said. "Whether you joked or not, I am now truly glad that you desire to stay."

Thus all was well. The fun and feasting began anew; but Pandarus, if he could have arranged it politely, would have rushed her off to bed at once. He said, "Lord, this is a terrible rain! This is good weather for sleeping; and I suggest that we soon begin. Niece, do you know where I shall put your bed, so that you will sleep where you and I will not be far apart, and so that you will not be troubled, I hope, by the noise of either rain or thunder? By God, right there in my little closet. In the outer room I alone will be guardian for all your women, who shall sleep easily and comfortably in this middle room which you see. As I said, you will be in the inner room, and if you sleep well tonight, then come back often, no matter what the weather is. Let us have the last glass of wine at once, and as soon as you wish we shall go to sleep. I think that will be best."

That was all, but soon afterwards they drank the wine and drew the curtains. Then everyone who had no further reason to remain there went out of the room. It rained increasingly harder, and the wind blew so unusually loud that one person could scarcely hear another. Then Pandarus, her uncle, mer-

Book Three

rily led Criseyde to her bedside, together with the women who usually attended her, and, as was proper, he took his leave, bowing low. He said, "All your women will be sleeping here just across from your door; when you wish any of them, you have only to call." So when she had gone to bed in the inner room, and her women had gone out to their place which I mentioned before, there was no more skipping or running about. If anyone were still stirring around, he was angrily told to go to bed so that those who wished to do so could sleep.

But when Pandarus, who knew well every step and every point in the old dance, saw that everything was well arranged, he thought that he would begin his work. Softly he unlatched the closet door without waiting longer, and sat down as still as a stone by Troilus. Briefly, in order to get at once to the point, he told Troilus all the details of his arrangement. Then he said, "Make ready at once, for you shall go into the bliss of heaven."

"Now, blessed Venus, send me grace," said Troilus. "Never yet did I have need of it before now, nor half the fear."

"Don't be a bit afraid; all will go just as you wish," said Pandarus. "As I hope to prosper, this night I shall make it go well, or cast all the gruel into the fire."

"Even so," prayed Troilus, "inspire me this night, blessed Venus, as surely as I serve you now and ever shall, more and more until I die. And, O happy goddess, if the aspects of Mars or of Saturn were bad when I was born, or if you were powerless at my birth, pray your father to turn all that evil to favor so that I may be in bliss. Do this for love of him you loved in the woods; I mean Adonis, who was killed by the boar. Help me also, O Jove, for the love of fair Europa whom you

90

Troilus and Criseyde

in the form of a bull took away. O Mars, you with your bloody cape, for the love of Venus do not hinder me! O Phebus, remember how Diana shut herself within the bark and became a laurel because of fear; yet for her love help me now in my time of need! Help me now also, Mercury, for the love of Herse, for whom Pallas was angry with Aglaurus! And Diana, I beseech you also not to be unsympathetic in this affair. O fatal sisters who spun my destiny before any garment was made for me, help me finish this work which has begun!"

"You wretched mouse's heart," said Pandarus, "are you afraid she will bite you? Why, put this fur cloak over your shirt and follow me, for I will take the blame. But wait and let me go a little ahead." With these words, he unlatched a trap door and led Troilus in by the cloak. The brisk wind blew so loud that one could hear no other noise. Those people who lay outside the door slept soundly. Then Pandarus very quietly went at once to the door near where they lay, and with no difficulty softly shut it. As he was stealthily returning, his niece awoke and asked, "Who is there?"

"Dear niece," he replied, "it is I. Do not wonder or be afraid." Then he came closer and whispered in her ear, "Say no word, I beg you, for love of God! Let no one rise and hear us talking."

"What, which way did you come in?" she asked. "How did you pass by without their knowing?"

"Through this secret trap door here," he replied.

"Let me call someone!" Criseyde said.

"God forbid that you should commit such folly," said Pandarus. "They might think things they never thought before. It is not good to wake a sleeping dog, nor to give a person cause

Book Three

for imagining. I guarantee that your women are all asleep and will sleep until the sun rises; for all they know, men could undermine the house. When my story is over, I shall go away just as I came, without their knowing. Now, niece, you should understand clearly that which all you women believe; if a woman keeps a man dangling a long time in love, calling him her sweetheart and dear one, and then hoodwinks him by loving another at the same time, she brings shame upon herself and does him an evil trick.

"Here is why I tell you all this: you know yourself as well as anyone how you have fully granted your love to Troilus, the worthiest of knights in this world, to whom you pledged your love in good faith; thus, unless he deserved it, you would never betray him as long as you live. It has happened this way since I left you: Troilus, to tell you bluntly, has come in all this rain through a gutter-pipe by a secret way into my room; by the faith I have in Priam of Troy, and as sure as I hope for happiness, no one except me knows of his coming. He has arrived in such pain and distress that, unless he is completely insane by now, he will soon go mad without God's help. Here is the cause of this: he says a friend told him that you love a man named Horastes, for grief at which this night shall be Troilus' last."

Criseyde, upon hearing all this strange news, felt a chill suddenly creep around her heart; sighing she sadly answered, "Alas, I thought no matter who told such tales my dear heart would not so easily consider me false! Alas, what harm mistaken notions do, for now I have lived too long! Horastes! Alas, and deceive Troilus? I do not know him, so help me God. What wicked person told him that? Now certainly, uncle, tomorrow, if I see him, I shall excuse myself as fully as a woman ever did, if he wishes." And with these words she sighed deeply.

"O God!" she continued, "thus is worldly happiness which the clerics call false felicity mingled with much bitterness! The condition of vain prosperity is full of anguish, God knows; either joys come not together, or else they are not lasting for anyone here. O brittle, unstable well-being in the happiness of man! No matter to what man you come or how you play, either he knows that you, joy, are mutable, or he knows it not; it must be one of the two. If he does not know it, how can he who is always in the darkness of ignorance say that he has true joy and happiness? But if he knows that happiness is transitory and that every worldly joy is fleeting, then every time he recalls that fact, the fear of losing happiness prevents his having perfect enjoyment. If he cares not a mite about losing his joy, then that joy seems worth little to him. Therefore, I shall state in this matter that certainly, for all I can see, there is no true well-being here in this world. But O you wicked serpent, jealousy, you misbelieving envious folly, why have you caused Troilus to distrust me, who never yet to my knowledge betrayed him?"

"Here is the way it happened—" said Pandarus.

"Why, uncle," she asked, "who told him this? Why does my dear heart believe it, alas?"

"You know, niece, how it is," he replied. "I hope all that is wrong will be straightened out. You can cure all this if you wish. Do just that, because I believe it is for the best."

"I shall do so tomorrow, certainly," she said. "As God is my witness, it shall be made clear."

Book Three

"Tomorrow? Alas, that would be a fine thing!" said Pandarus. "No, no, that will not do, for as the clerics write, niece, danger is increased by delay. No, such waiting is not worth a berry. Niece, I think there is a time for all things. For when a room or hall is on fire, there is greater need to rescue valuables at once than to dispute and to ask everyone how the candle fell into the straw. Ah, bless me! Despite all that talk the harm is done and—farewell valuables! And niece, do not be aggrieved, but if you allow him to pass all night in this woe, so help me God, you never loved him; I dare say that, since we two are alone. But I know well that you will not do such a thing. You are too wise to be so foolish as to place his life in jeopardy all night."

"I never loved him? By God, I don't think you ever loved anything so much!" said Criseyde.

"Now by my thrift," said Pandarus, "that shall be seen! For since you take me as your example, you should know that if for all the treasure in the city of Troy I allowed Troilus to remain all night in sorrow, I would pray God that I would never again enjoy happiness. Look, now; if you who are his love should put his life in jeopardy because of a trifling matter, by God above, such delay arises not from folly but from malice, if I speak truly. Why, bluntly, if you leave him in distress, you are neither generous nor courteous."

Criseyde then answered, "Will you do one thing which will put an end to all his suffering? Take this blue ring to him, for there is nothing which would please him more or sooner quiet his anxiety, except me. Tell my dear heart that his sorrow is causeless, as shall be apparent tomorrow."

Troilus and Criseyde

"A ring?" cried Pandarus. "Indeed, may the hazelwoods shake with laughter! Yes, niece, that ring must have a stone in it which would make dead men come alive; and I don't believe you have a ring which can do that. All discretion has gone out of your head; I see that now, and it is a pity. O lost time! Well may you curse sloth! Do you not realize that noble and high spirits do not grieve or stop grieving easily? If a fool were in a jealous rage, I would not care a mite for his sorrow, but only grant him a few kind words some other day when I might meet him; but this matter is wholly different. Troilus is so gentle and tender-hearted that he will avenge his sorrow with his death. For you can be sure that no matter how great his pain, he will not upbraid you with jealous words. Therefore, niece, before his heart breaks, speak to him yourself about this matter; with one word you can gladden his heart. I have told you what danger he is in, and that his coming here is unknown to any other person. Indeed, there can be no harm or sin; I myself shall be with you all this night. You know also that he is your own suitor and that by rights you must trust him; now I am eager to lead him here when you so desire."

This misunderstanding was so piteous to hear, and also seemed so true at its face value, and Troilus, her knight, was so dear to her, what with his secret coming and the private place, that, all things considered, it is no great wonder that she did him a favor, since she did all for the best.

Criseyde answered, "As surely as I hope God will bring my soul to rest, I feel great woe for him! And, uncle, I am certainly eager to do what is best, if I knew what to do. But I am puzzled as to whether you should stay here or go for him; I am at my wit's end."

Book Three

"Well, niece, will you listen?" asked Pandarus. "Being puzzled is called 'the torment of wretches.' It seems difficult because through sloth or other wilful faults wretches will not learn. That which they say is not worth two beans. But you are wise; that which we have to do with is neither difficult nor subtle to understand."

"Then, uncle," said Criseyde, "do as you wish. But before he comes, I shall first get up. And, for the love of God, since all my trust is placed in you two, who are both wise, work so discreetly now that I may keep my honor and Troilus may have pleasure. For in this I am completely under your control."

"That is well said, dear niece," answered Pandarus. "Blessings on your wise gentle heart! But lie still and receive him right where you are; there is no need to move because of him. For the love of God, each of you ease the other's hurt. Venus, I praise you, for soon I hope we shall all three be merry."

Troilus approached and at once fell on his knees by the head of her bed; he greeted his lady in his best fashion. But, Lord, she suddenly blushed! Though her head were to be cut off, she could not bring out a single word correctly, so embarrassed was she at his sudden coming. Pandarus, who was extremely sensitive to every situation, at once began to jest, and said, "Niece, see how this lord can kneel! Now, on your word, is he not a gentleman?" Then he ran for a cushion, saying, "Kneel on this as long as you like; may God soon put your hearts at rest!"

Criseyde did not command Troilus to rise. I cannot say whether her sympathy caused her to forget propriety, or whether she took his action as a courteous duty. But I find

Troilus and Criseyde

that she did him the pleasure of kissing him, although she sighed deeply, and bade him be seated without more ado.

Pandarus said, "Now you have begun well. Niece, let him sit on the side of your bed, so that you can hear each other better." With these words Pandarus moved over to the fire, took a light, and settled himself as if to read an old romance.

Criseyde, the true lady of Troilus, knew herself fully innocent; though she thought that her servant and her knight should not have believed any untruth of her, nevertheless she considered his distress and that love often causes such folly, and spoke thus to him concerning his jealousy: "See, my heart, because of the power of love, against which no man may or should make resistance, and also because I felt and saw from your great service and faithfulness to me that your heart was truly all mine, I was led to take pity on your suffering. I have always realized your goodness, my knight and dear heart, for which I thank you as best I am able, though that is less than you deserve. I, to the full extent of my wit and power, have been and ever shall be true to you with all my heart, no matter how much I suffer as a result. And without doubt, that will be proved to you.

"But, my heart, all the details necessary in this matter we shall discuss so that you need not grieve, even if I have to plead with you in person. For at last I mean to kill completely the pain which holds your heart and mine in heaviness, and to redress every wrong. My dear one, I do not know how or why jealousy, that wicked serpent, has crept into you without cause; I am eager to rid you of that evil. Alas, that he without opposition could have his refuge in so noble a place; may Jove at once erase him from your heart! But, O Jove, creator

97

of nature, is this an honor to your deity that innocent folk suffer injury and the guilty go completely unpunished? O that it were possible for me to complain to you because the undeserving suffer jealousy! About that I would object strongly to you! Also, my woe is this: folk used to say 'Jealousy is love,' and would fully excuse a bushel of envy if one grain of love were stuffed in it; but high God who sits aloft knows whether that is nearer love, or hate, or anger. That quality should bear its proper name.

"Certainly some kinds of jealousy are more excusable than others; for example, that for which there is cause and where the imagination is so restrained by piety that almost nothing amiss is said or done, and the jealous one suffers alone in his distress; that I excuse as courtesy. Some jealousy, however, is so filled with fury and hatred that it overcomes restraint. But you are not like that, dear heart, for which I thank God. Therefore, I call the feeling which causes you this distress illusion only, born of an abundance of love and concern. I am extremely sorry for it, but not angry. On behalf of my honor and the comfort of your heart, for the love of God put this matter to a proper test, either by ordeal or by oath, by chance or what you like. If I prove guilty, then kill me! Alas, what more can I do or say?" With these words a few bright tears fell from her eyes, and she continued, "Now God, you know that neither in thought nor deed was Criseyde ever yet untrue to Troilus." Then she lay her head upon the pillow, covered it with the sheet, sighed sorely, and held her peace. She spoke not one word more.

Now may God help to extinguish all this sorrow! I hope that He will, for He is the most able to do it. I have often

Troilus and Criseyde

seen a very misty dawn followed by a bright summer's day, and green May follows after winter. Men observe every day and also read in stories that victories follow brisk skirmishes.

You can be sure that Troilus did not wish to go to sleep when he heard her words. For to see and hear Criseyde, his lady, weeping was far worse to him than being beaten with a stick. With every drop which fell from Criseyde's eyes, he felt the fear of death clutch at his heart. And in his mind he began to curse the time that he had come there and that he was born. For now a bad situation is made worse, and all the labor he had earlier done he considered lost. He assumed he was ruined. "O Pandarus," he thought, "alas, your trickery serves for nothing, woe to me!" Then he hung his head, fell to his knees, and sorrowfully sighed. What could he say? He felt as if he were dead, for she who should lighten his cares was angry. Nevertheless, as soon as he could speak, he said thus, "God knows that when all the details of this scheme become known, I will not be blamed." At that, grief so encompassed his heart that not a tear fell from his eyes, and his every feeling became so knotted that he was dazed. His sorrow, his fear, and all his other reactions fled, and suddenly he fell down in a faint.

One could then see no little sorrow, but all was hushed and Pandarus quickly approached and said, "Quiet, niece, or we are lost. Do not be afraid!" In the end, it is certain, Pandarus finally placed Troilus in the bed and asked, "O thief, is this the heart of a man?" Then he removed all Troilus' clothes except his shirt, saying, "Niece, unless you aid us now, alas, your own Troilus is lost!"

Book Three

"Certainly, I would do so willingly if I knew how," she said. "Alas that I was born!"

"Well, niece," urged Pandarus, "if you wish to pull out the thorn which sticks in his heart, say 'All is forgiven,' and put an end to this business!"

"Yes," she replied, "I would rather do that than have all the goods under the sun." Then she swore in Troilus' ear, "Truly, dear heart, I am not angry; accept my pledge!" and many another oath. "Now speak to me, for it is I, Criseyde!" she continued. But all was in vain; he heard nothing.

They felt his pulse, rubbed the palms of his hands, and wet his temples. She frequently kissed him to bring him to life; and, in brief, she did all she could to revive him. At last, he began to breathe deeply and, waking soon afterwards from his faint, he recovered his composure and reason. But he was dreadfully abashed, and with a sigh when he was fully awake, he said, "O mercy, God, what has happened? Why do you seem so troubled?"

Criseyde then answered, "Is this the action of a man? Are you not ashamed, Troilus, to act thus?" Then she placed her arm around him, forgave everything, and kissed him many times. He thanked her, spoke to her and asked her about those matters necessary to put his heart at ease. She answered as she wished, and began to entertain him with kindly words, and comfort his sorrows.

Pandarus said, "For all I can determine, there is no need here for this light or for me. Light is not good for the eyes of sick folk! But, for the love of God, since you have now reached this happy situation, do not permit any sad thoughts

Troilus and Criseyde

to hang in your two hearts." With that he took the candle over to the chimney.

Soon after this, although it was not necessary, she demanded such oaths as she wished from Troilus. She did not think that fear or any other reason should cause her to force him to rise from the bed. In many a case lesser things than oaths may suffice, for no man in love, I believe, intends to be anything except noble. But, in effect, she wished to know at once of what man, where, and also why Troilus was jealous, since there was no real cause for it. She bade him tell her immediately what signs made him believe this thing. Unless he could do so, she insisted that this was a trick done out of malice to deceive her.

Beyond any doubt Troilus was compelled to do as his lady bade. As the lesser of two evils, he had to feign an answer. He told her that when she was at such-and-such a feast she could at least have glanced at him—I do not know what he answered, but it was a likely story, such as one who had to fish for an excuse would tell.

She answered, "Sweet, even if it were true, what harm was there in that, since I meant no evil? For by God who redeemed both of us, my intention is pure in all things. Such arguments are not worth a bean. Do you wish to act like a jealous child? Now you deserve to be whipped."

Then Troilus sighed sadly, for he thought his heart would break if she were angry, and he said, "Alas, have mercy on my great grief, Criseyde, my sweetheart! If I were at all wrong in what I said, I shall not trespass again. Do what you like; I am completely at your mercy."

Book Three

She replied, "Pity for guilt; that is to say, I forgive all. But do not ever forget this night, and beware that you never again do amiss."

"No, dear heart, I shall never again do so," he answered.

"Now," she said, "since I have scolded you, forgive me, sweetheart."

Troilus, surprised by this happiness, placed everything in God's hands, as does one who means only well. Suddenly revived, he clasped her tightly in his arms. Then Pandarus, ever helpful, prepared for sleep, and said, "If you are wise don't make any noise, lest other people awake."

What can the poor lark say when the sparrow-hawk has caught it in its claws? I know nothing more, but for those who consider this tale a sweet one I must, though I waste a year, tell something of what my author relates about the happiness of these two, just as I have told you in detail of their sadness.

Criseyde, when she felt herself thus embraced in his arms, began to tremble like an aspen leaf—so write the scholars in their old books. But Troilus, cured of all his cold cares, began to thank the seven blessed gods. Thus do various woes lead folk to heaven. Troilus, clasping her in his arms, said, "O sweet, as I hope ever to thrive, you are now caught; now we two are all alone! Yield, for there is no other remedy!"

To this Criseyde at once answered, "If I had not before this decided to yield, sweetheart, I would certainly not be here now!"

Oh, true it is that in order to be cured of a fever or of any other great sickness, men must drink a bitter drink, as is often seen; and in order to have happiness men drink often of pain and great distress. In this instance, I mean that all Troilus'

Troilus and Criseyde

cure has come through suffering. But now sweetness seems sweeter because bitterness was earlier tasted. For out of woe, they now float in bliss such as they never felt since they were born. Certainly, this is better than if they were both lost. For the love of God, let every woman be advised to act thus, if the necessity arises.

Criseyde, free of every fear and worry, since she had ample cause to trust him, made him such cheer as was a joy to see, when she had understood his faithful and pure intent. They were entwined in each other's arms just as the sweet woodbine wraps itself with many a twist about a tree. Like the young fearful nightingale which halts her song when she hears a shepherd nearby, or any person moving through the hedges, and then sings out clearly when her fears are quieted, so Criseyde when her doubts vanished opened her heart and told him her feeling.

Troilus, who now had his dear lady, for all the world felt happiness similar to that of a man who sees his death planned—and die he must, so far as he knows—and then suddenly he escapes and is led from death to safety. May God grant that we never meet worse fortune! Troilus often stroked her small arms, her straight soft back, and her slender, firm, smooth white sides; many times he blessed her snowy throat and her small round breasts. Thus he delighted in this heaven, kissed her a thousand times, and for sheer joy scarcely knew what to do.

"O Love, O Charity!" he cried. "May your mother, sweet Venus, the well-wishing planet, be praised next after you! After that I greet you, Hymen. For never was a man so beholden to you gods as I, whom you have led from cold cares.

Book Three

Benign Love, you holy binder of creatures, whoever seeks grace and does not honor you, then his desire attempts to fly without wings. For if you do not wish with your bounty to help those who serve best and labor most, then all is lost, I am certainly willing to state, unless your kindness surpasses their merit. In my case you have helped me, the least deserving in the list of those who serve you, when I was likely to die; and you have placed me in so lofty a place that I know only that no happiness equals mine. Praise and reverence are due your generosity and your excellence!"

With that he kissed Criseyde, at which she certainly felt no discomfort. Then he said, "Now, would to God I knew, sweetheart, how I might please you. What man was ever so fortunate as I, to whom the fairest and best woman I ever saw deigns to give her heart? Here men can see that mercy goes beyond justice. My case proves that, for I am unworthy of the love of so sweet a person; but, my dear, I beg you in your benignity to think that, though I am now unworthy, I must needs improve in some ways through the ennobling service I pay you. For the love of God, my dear lady, since God has created me to serve you—I mean He willed you to be my star and to have the power of life and death over me—teach me how I can deserve your thanks, so that I do not cause you any displeasure through my ignorance. Certainly, perfect one, I dare state that you shall find me faithful and diligent all my life. I will surely never do that which you forbid; and if I do, either in or out of your presence, for the love of God have me killed for the deed if you wish."

Criseyde replied, "Certainly, my own heart's desire, my foundation of comfort, my dear heart, I thank you, for in your

104

Troilus and Criseyde

words I place full faith! But let us drop this discussion; all that was needed here has been said. In a word, welcome without regret, my knight, my peace, my everything!"

I have not the ability to tell of her delight or of the least of her joys. But you who have been at the feast of such happiness judge whether or not these two wished to play! I know nothing except that on this night these same two, between fear and security, felt the full value of love. O blissful night, how merry you were for both these two people who had sought you so long! Why have I not bought such a night with my soul, yes, or at least the smallest joy that was there? Away, you foul disdain and fear; let these two dwell in that high heavenly bliss which is beyond my description! But the truth is that although I cannot tell everything which my excellent author includes, yet as God is my witness I have given and shall give his full meaning. If I have added any good word in reverence of Love, do with it just as you wish. For I speak all my words here and everywhere under correction of those of you who have feeling in the art of love; and I place all at your discretion and beg you to increase or diminish my language as you see fit. But now back to my earlier purpose.

These two lovers wrapped in each other's arms were so loath to part that it seemed to each that he was being kidnapped. Their greatest fear was that all this night was only a foolish dream; as a result, each of them often said, "O sweet one, do I embrace you thus, or do I dream it?" And Lord, Troilus looked so steadily at her that his eyes never left her face. He said, "O dear heart, is it possibly true that you are here in this place?"

Book Three

"Yes, my heart," she replied, "and I thank God for his kindness." She then kissed him, and for sheer joy he did not know where his spirit was.

Troilus frequently kissed her two eyes and said, "O clear eyes, it was you who caused me such woe, you humble traps of my dear lady! Though there is mercy written in your gaze, the text, God knows, is truly hard to find. How could you bind me without chains?" At that he clasped her in his arms and sighed at least a hundred times, not such sad sighs as those made by woeful men or by folk who are sick, but comfortable sighs showing pleasure and satisfaction. He could not experience enough of such sighing.

Soon after this they discussed many things which concerned their love, and playfully exchanged their rings. I can tell no exact details about this, but I know very well that Criseyde pinned to his shirt a gold and azure brooch in which was set a heart-shaped ruby. Lord, do you think a covetous person or a wretch, who curses love and holds it in disdain, was ever yet granted such delight from the pennies he can scrape together and squeeze, as there is in certain love situations? No, surely not, for so help me God, no niggard can have such perfect joy. They will say "Yes"; but, Lord, how they lie, those nervous wretches, full of woe and fear! They call love a madness or folly, but I shall tell you what happens to them: they are forced to give up wine and live in woe; may God send them bad luck and advance every faithful lover! Would to God that those wretches who despise the service of love had ears as long as covetous Midas, and had drunk as hot and strong a drink as Crassus took for his wicked purpose; they would

Troilus and Criseyde

learn that they, not the lovers whom they consider foolish,
are wrong.

These two of whom I tell you, Troilus and Criseyde, began
to talk and to play, after their hearts were filled with mutual
trust; also they rehearsed how, when, and where they first were
acquainted, and every sorrow and fear they had endured. But,
thank God, all such sadness was now turned to joy. Each
time that they spoke of past suffering, the discussion was inter-
rupted by kissing, and new happiness at once arose. They did
all they could, now that they were united, to recover happiness
and to be satisfied, and they counterbalanced every sorrow
with joy. It is not reasonable for me to speak of sleep, for
it is not in accord with my material. God knows, they paid
little heed to it! But lest this night, so dear to them, should
be lacking in any way, it was filled with all that has to do with
joy and nobility.

When the rooster, the timepiece of nature, began to beat
on his breast and then to crow; when Lucifer, messenger of
the day, rose and threw forth his beams; when Jupiter rose in
the east, recognized by whoever knew him; then Criseyde with
a heavy heart said to Troilus: "My heart's life, my faith, and
my pleasure, alas that I was born, for I am saddened that daylight will part us! For it is time to rise and leave, or else I am
lost forever! O night, alas, why will you not hover over us
as long as when Jove lay with Alcmena? O black night, as
folks may read in books, you were created by God to hide this
world at certain times with your black clothing, so that men
might experience rest; beasts might well complain, and people
scold you, because you flee and steal our rest when day comes
to break us with labor. Rash night, alas, you do your work

Book Three

too quickly. Because of your haste and unkindness, may God, Creator of nature, bind you so tightly to our hemisphere that you will no longer be able to disappear underground. For now, because you rush away from Troy, I must quickly lose my happiness!"

Troilus seemed to feel the bloody drops melt from his heart with pity and distress at her words; he had never felt such sadness following great happiness. He consequently crushed Criseyde, his dear lady, in his arms and said, "O cruel day, revealer of the joy which night and love have secretly and securely hidden, cursed be your coming to Troy, for every corner is touched by your bright eyes! Envious day, why do you wish to be a spy? What have you lost? Why do you seek out this place? May God in his kindness quench your light! Alas, disdainful day, what injury have lovers done you? May you suffer the pains of hell, for you have slain and will slay many a lover. Your coming leaves them no place to go. Why do you offer your light for sale here? Go sell it to those who engrave small seals; we don't want you, for we need no daylight."

Also he chided Titan, the sun, saying, "O fool, well may men hate you, since you have the dawn by your side all night and then allow her to leave you so early, and thus to disturb lovers. Why, stay there in your bed! And you also, Morning! I pray God to send sorrow to you both!"

Then he sighed sorely and said, "My bright lady, the well and root of my happiness and sorrow, my good one Criseyde, must I rise, alas, must I do that? I now feel that my heart must break in two. For how can I retain life for an hour, since all the life I have is that spent with you? What shall

Troilus and Criseyde

I do? Certainly, I do not know when I shall again see the time that I am in such a situation as this night with you. God knows how my life can continue, since desire so bites me right now that I shall die at once unless I remain with you. How can I live long away from you? Nevertheless, my own bright lady, if it were so that I knew surely that I, your humble servant and your knight, was as firmly set in your heart as you are in mine,—a thing I would truly rather know than to own two worlds—then could I better endure all my pain."

Crisyede at once gave answer to that, and with a sigh she said, "O dear heart, this game has surely progressed so far now that Phebus shall fall from his sphere, and every eagle be companion to a dove, and every rock move from its place before Troilus goes out of Criseyde's heart. You are so deeply graven in my heart that, even though I wished to put you out of my thoughts, as surely as I hope God will save my soul, I could not do it, but would die of the pain.

"For the love of God who created us, do not let any other such fantasy creep into your mind, lest thereby you cause my death! I beseech you to keep me as firmly in mind as I do you; if I am sure of that, God cannot add a single point to my joy. But, my heart, without more discussion, be true to me; otherwise it would be a shame, for I am yours, by God and on my word! Be glad, therefore, and live in faith! I never said these things before now, and never shall to any other. If you would gladly return to me as soon as you leave, I wish as much as you that it were possible, as surely as I hope God will bring my heart to rest!" Then she took him in her arms and kissed him often.

Book Three

Troilus arose against his will, since it had to be so. He dressed rapidly, took his dear lady in his arms a hundred times, and rushed away, saying in a voice which showed his bleeding heart, "Farewell, dear sweetheart, may God grant us safety and a meeting in the near future!"

She made no answer to this, so bitterly was she pained by his departure. Troilus went to his palace, truly as woebegone as she. The pain of his sharp desire to be with her again so wrung him that he could not put it out of his mind. Upon arrival at his royal palace, he quietly crept into his bed to sleep for a long time, as was his custom. But all was in vain; he could lie there with eyes closed, but he could not sleep because the thought of her for whom desire in him burned was a thousand times stronger than he knew. All her words and facial expressions he turned up and down in his mind, and the least thing which gave him pleasure was firmly implanted in his memory. Truly, these recollections caused his desire to burn with renewed fury, and his lust to grow even more than formerly; yet he took no heed.

In exactly the same manner Criseyde enclosed within her heart Troilus' bravery, his gaiety, wisdom, and courtesy; remembering how she had met him, she thanked Love for her good fortune. She wished to have her lover again with her so that she might cheer him.

In the morning Pandarus came to his niece; greeting her pleasantly, he said, "It rained so hard all last night that I fear, sweet niece, you had little opportunity to sleep and dream The rain kept me awake all night, and I think certain ones of us have headaches today." Then drawing nearer, he continued,

Troilus and Criseyde

"How goes everything this merry morning? Niece, how is it with you?"

"No better because of you, fox that you are," retorted Criseyde. "May God send you worries! So help me God, I think you caused all this business, despite your innocent words. Oh, he who sees you knows you but slightly." Then she hid her face under the sheet and blushed with shame.

Pandarus peeked under the sheet and said, "Niece, if I deserve death, take this sword and cut off my head!" Then he quickly slipped his arm around her neck and kissed her.

I pass over all that which there is no need to tell. Why, God forgave those who killed Him, and Criseyde also forgave Pandarus and began to joke with him, for she really had no cause to blame him. But—to continue this story briefly—she went to her home in due time; Pandarus had seen his purpose wholly fulfilled.

Now let us turn back to Troilus, who lay restless in his bed all day. He privately sent for Pandarus to come to him in all possible haste. The latter soon arrived; never had he refused Troilus anything. Sitting down on the side of the bed, he soberly greeted Troilus. With all the affection of a friend's love which one can imagine, Troilus fell on his knees before Pandarus. And before he rose from this spot, he thanked him as best he could a hundred times, and blessed the day that Pandarus was born to lead him from distress.

He said, "O best of friends who ever lived, truly you have brought my soul out of Phlegethon, the fiery flood of hell, to its rest in heaven. If I should lose my life a thousand times in one day serving you, it would not suffice to repay you. I dare wager my life that the sun which looks upon the whole

111

Book Three

world never saw anyone so fair and good as she, to whom I belong and shall belong completely until I die. Since I am thus hers, thanked be the high nobility of Love and also your kind helpfulness. It is no little thing which you have given me, and for which I shall all my life be indebted to you. Why? Because through your help I live; otherwise, I would have long ago been dead." With these words he lay down.

Pandarus soberly let him have his say and then replied, "My dear friend, if I have been at all helpful to you, God knows I am as glad of it as any man could be. But do not be aggrieved if I say to you that you should beware of mischance, so that you do not cause the bliss which you now enjoy to change. For the worst characteristic of Fortune's sharp adversity is for a man to remember his former prosperity when it has passed. You are wise enough not to make that mistake. Be not too rash, even though you are now well placed, for if you are rash, you will certainly be led to harm. You are now happy; remain that way. For as surely as every fire is red, it takes as much skill to hold a thing as to win it. Always keep a tight rein over your speech and your desire; for worldly joys are kept in place by only a thin chain, which often breaks easily. Therefore, it is necessary for you to proceed carefully."

Troilus answered, "My dear friend, as God is my witness I hope that I shall so conduct myself that I shall be guilty of losing nothing, and that my rashness shall not cause grief. There is no need for further guidance in this matter. You know my heart well, Pandarus, and, God knows, you need not worry much about this."

Then Troilus reported all the events of his happy night. He told why and how he had first suffered, and then he said,

Troilus and Criseyde

"Friend, as I am a true knight, and by the faith I have in God and you, I never burned so hotly as now. The more desire bites me to love her best, the more it pleases me. I do not myself fully understand what it is, but now I feel a new quality; yes, it is entirely different from anything I ever felt before."

Pandarus answered, "He who can once manage to come into the bliss of heaven feels otherwise, I dare say, than when he first heard that bliss described."

Here is one word in summary: Troilus could not have enough of discussing this matter, praising to Pandarus the generosity of his dear lady, and thanking Pandarus for his help. This tale seemed ever-new to Troilus, until night caused the two friends to separate.

Soon after this Fortune willed that the happy occasion had arrived for Troilus to be told to meet his lady Criseyde in the same place as they had met formerly. As a result, he felt his heart float in joy, and faithfully began to praise all the gods. Now let's see whether he can be merry!

The same manner of arrival for him and for her, as had been used in the first instance, was repeated; there is no need to explain it again. But—to get to the point—Pandarus led the two of them to bed in joy and safety when they so desired. Thus they were in peace and comfort. Since they were together, there is no need for you to ask me whether they were happy. For if all went well during their first meeting, this second one was a thousand times better. There is no question about that. Every sorrow and every fear had vanished, and both certainly possessed, it seemed to them, as much joy as a heart might hold. Such a statement is no trifling matter; it is beyond the understanding of ordinary folk. For each of

Book Three

these two obeyed the other's wishes. Felicity, which is so commended by these wise clerics, is too small a word for this situation. This joy cannot be set down with ink; it surpasses all imagination.

But cruel day—woe to its coming—approached, as they could tell from the usual signs; consequently, they felt themselves mortally wounded. They were so sad that their complexions changed, and once again they hated the daylight, calling it an envious traitor or worse, and bitterly cursing it. Troilus said, "Alas, I am now aware that Pyroeis and the three other swift steeds which draw the sun's chariot have approached by some by-path in order to spite me, and will soon cause it to be day. Since the sun makes such haste to rise, I shall never make a sacrifice to him."

The light made it necessary for them to leave soon, and when their encouraging speech was over, they parted quickly; as was their custom, they set a time for their next meeting. Many a night they spent together in this fashion. Thus did Fortune for a time bring Criseyde and this son of the king of Troy to happiness.

Troilus now passed his days in satisfaction, in happiness, and in song. He spent freely, jousted, made feasts; he gave generously, changed clothes often, and kept about him always a world of people, who, as suited his nature, were the gayest and best he could find. Throughout the world his reputation for honor and largess grew so great that it reached up to the gates of heaven. He was so happily in love that, I think, he decided in his heart that there was no lover in the world so well situated as he; thus did love please him. The attractiveness or beauty which nature had given to any other lady could

Troilus and Criseyde

in no way untie the net with which Criseyde had ensnared his heart. That net was so closely knit and meshed that it could never be untied, whatever happened. He would often take Pandarus by the hand and lead him into the garden. Then he would speak such praise of Criseyde, of her womanhood and her beauty, that without doubt it was heavenly to hear his words. Also he would sing in this manner:

THE SONG OF TROILUS

Love, who has control of earth and sea,
Love, whose commands come from high heaven,
Love, who with a wholesome alliance
Keeps people joined, and guides them as he wishes,
Love, who knits the law of companionship,
And causes couples to live in strength,
Bind this accord, of which I have told and tell.

That the stable world with faith
Holds its diverse seasons in concord,
That elements which are so diverse
Keep a bond enduring perpetually,
That Phebus can bring forth his rosy day,
And that the moon has lordship over the nights,—
All this does Love; may his powers be ever praised!

And the sea, so greedy to overflow,
Thus constrains for a definite purpose
Its terrible floods, so that they do not rise
To drench earth and all forevermore;
But, if Love should loose his bridle,
All that now loves would leap asunder,
And all that Love now holds together would be lost.

Book Three

O would to God, author of nature,
That Love with his bond should strongly desire
To encircle all hearts, and bind them fast,
So that from his bond none could find a way out;
And cold hearts, I wish that he would twist them
So as to make them love and always desire to pity
Suffering hearts, and to protect those who are faithful!

As for all that was necessary during the siege, Troilus was always first in deeds of arms—unless the books lie—except for Hector, who was the most feared of all. This increase in hardiness and strength came to him through love and a desire to win his lady's thanks, which had altered his spirit completely. In time of truce, he would ride out hawking, or else hunt the boar, bear, or lion; he let the smaller animals go free. When he came riding back into town, his lady often looked down from her window, as fresh as a falcon just coming from the coop, to give him the best of greetings. His talk was chiefly about love and virtue; and all miserable qualities he despised.

Doubtless, there was no need to beg him to honor those who were noble, or to comfort those in distress; and he was happy when he heard that any person who was a lover fared well. For, to tell the truth, he considered every person lost who was not a servant of Love; I mean those folk who ought properly to have been so. In addition to this, so well could he speak of sentiment, and in so unusual a fashion did he dress, that every lover thought highly of whatever Troilus said or did. Though he came of royal blood, he never cared to attack anyone as a result of pride. He was kind to everyone, for which he everywhere received thanks. Thus Love—praised be

Troilus and Criseyde

his grace—caused Troilus to flee from Pride, Envy, Wrath, Avarice, and every other vice.

You shining lady, daughter of Diana, also you blind and winged son, Cupid, and you nine sisters who live by Helicon on the hill Parnassus, thus far have you deigned to guide me; I know no more, but since you will leave, may you be praised forever without end. Through you I have told fully in my song the result and happiness of Troilus' service to Love, although there was some distress included, which my author desired to describe. I now end my third book in this fashion, and Troilus in joy and quiet is with his own sweetheart, Criseyde.

HERE ENDS BOOK III

Here Begins Book IV

HOWEVER, sad to say, such happiness lasts all too short a time, thanks be to Fortune who seems most faithful when she wishes to beguile, and can so ensnare fools with her song that she, common traitress, captures and blinds them! Then, when a person is thrown from her wheel, she laughs and sneers at him. She now began to turn her face away from Troilus and paid him no heed, but cast him completely out of his lady's grace, and set Diomede up on her wheel. For this my heart now begins to bleed, and my pen, alas, with which I am writing, trembles with fear of that which I must compose.

The subject of my book must henceforth be how Criseyde forsook Troilus, or was at least unnatural toward him, as the people from whom I learned the story wrote it. Alas, that they should have found reason to speak evil of her; and if they tell lies against her, certainly they should be blamed. O you Erinnyes, the three daughters of Night, who lament in endless torture: Megaera, Alecto, and Tisiphone; and you cruel Mars, also, father to Quirinus, help me finish this fourth book, so that here Troilus' loss of life and love together will be fully shown.

As I have said earlier, the strong Greek host lay siege to Troy, and it happened when Phebus shone from the breast of Hercules' Lion, that Hector one day planned with many other

Troilus and Criseyde

bold knights to fight the Greeks, as was his custom, in order to cause them as much grief as he could. I do not know how many days passed between his making this plan and the fulfillment of it, but one day he and the others went forth from the town, well-armed, bright, and shining, with spears and large bows in hand. Without further delay they met their enemies face to face on the battlefield. Both sides fought all day long with sharply ground spears, with arrows, darts, swords, and cruel maces; many a man and horse was felled, and many a head split open with axes. But in the last skirmish, to tell the truth, the Trojans fought so poorly that at nightfall they were forced to flee homeward defeated.

On this day Antenor was captured, despite the efforts of Polydamas or Mnestheus, Zanthippus, Sarpedon, Polymnestor, Polytes, or even the Trojan knight Riphaeus, and other lesser knights such as Phebuseus. As a result, the folk of Troy began that day to fear the loss of a great part of their happiness. Priam granted, at the request of the Greeks, a period of truce, and discussions were begun for the exchange of prisoners, important and otherwise; large sums would be given in exchange for surplus prisoners. This truce was at once made known to all the Trojans and their besiegers, and soon the news reached the ears of Calchas. When he learned that such discussions would be held, he went immediately to push himself into the assembly of older lords and sat down there, as was his custom. With a pleading countenance he asked them to do him the favor and honor, for the love of God, of being quiet and listening to him.

Then he said, "You see, my lords, I was a Trojan, as you no doubt know. If you recall, I am Calchas, who was the first to

Book Four

give sympathy to your cause and to tell you that you would
succeed. For beyond doubt, in time Troy will be burned by
you and razed to the ground. I have before now explained
to you just how to conquer this city and thus accomplish all
your desires. I believe, my lords, that you know these things.
Because the Greeks were so dear to me, I came in person to
teach you how best to accomplish them, caring not so much
for my treasures or my money as for your prospering. Thus
I left all my goods and came to you, thinking thereby to please
you, lords. But I am not concerned about all my losses; I am
willing, I swear, for your sake to lose everything I had in Troy,
except the daughter whom I left there, alas, sleeping at home,
while I stole out of the city. O stern, cruel father that I was!
How could I have had then so cruel a heart? Alas, that I did
not bring her in her night-dress! My sorrow is so great because
of this that I will not live another day, unless you lords take
pity upon me.

"Until now I have held my peace, because I saw no opportunity earlier of rescuing her. But now or never, if you are willing, I can soon have her here with me. O help me! Among all
this crowd, take pity on this old prisoner in distress, since on
your account I have all my sadness. You have now captured
and imprisoned many Trojans, and if you will do so, my child
may be redeemed with one of them. For the love of God,
be so generous as to give me one of these many prisoners!
Why should you deny my request, since you are going to
capture both the city and its inhabitants soon? On peril of
my life, I do not lie; Apollo has faithfully revealed this fact
to me. I have also found it to be true by astronomy, by lots,
and by augury. Thus I dare state that the time is near when

Troilus and Criseyde

fire and flame shall spread through all the city, and Troy will be reduced to dead ashes. For it is certain that both Phebus and Neptune, the makers of the walls of Troy, are so angry with the Trojans that they will bring the city to confusion, as revenge against King Laomedon, because he would not pay them their dues; for that reason, Troy shall be burned."

As he spoke, humble in words and also in manner, the salty tears poured from the two eyes of this old gray man, down each of his cheeks. He besought their help for so long a time that, to put an end to his terrible grief, they simply gave him Antenor. Who was happy then except Calchas? He soon explained his wishes to those Greeks who were to treat with the Trojans, and begged them often to bring back King Thoas and Criseyde in exchange for Antenor. When King Priam sent a safe-conduct, the ambassadors immediately left for Troy.

As soon as their business had been stated, aged King Priam convened his parliament in full meeting. I shall tell you the final decision: the ambassadors were definitely told that the proposed exchange of prisoners pleased the Trojans well. Then the ambassadors proceeded with the details. Troilus was present in the assembly when Criseyde was demanded in exchange for Antenor. At once he changed color, as if he were almost slain by those words. Nevertheless, he remained silent, lest people should detect his affection. With a manly heart he hid his sorrow and, filled with anxiety and horrible fear, he awaited the lords' reply. If they agreed, God forbid, to her exchange, Troilus thought he must then be concerned with two matters: first, how to save her reputation; and second, how he might best oppose the exchange.

Book Four

Troilus thought hard about all these things. Love made him eager to force her to remain, and to die rather than see her go. But, on the other hand, reason said to him, "Do not do anything without her consent, lest she become your enemy because of your actions, and say that through your meddling the love of you two, hitherto concealed, has become known widely." Thus Troilus decided that, though the lords agreed that she should go, it would be best for him not to oppose their decision until he had discussed matters with his lady. Then, when she had told him her reaction, he would work quickly, even if all the world stood against him.

Hector, when he heard the Greeks propose to exchange Antenor for Criseyde, was not in agreement. Soberly he said, "Sirs, she is no prisoner; I do not know who charged you with such a proposal but, for my part, you may tell them straightway that it is not our custom here to sell women."

At once a clamor arose among the people, as fierce as when straw is set on fire. For evil fortune wished in this instance that they should desire their own ruin. "Hector," they said, "what spirit inspires you to shield this woman and cause us to lose Antenor, who is so wise and bold a knight? You have chosen the wrong answer. Anyone can see that we have need of fighters. He is one of our town's greatest. O Hector, put aside your fancies! O King Priam, we say that our unanimous vote is to let Criseyde go." Then they begged for Antenor's deliverance.

O Lord Juvenal, true is your opinion that folk so little understand what they should seek that they do not see their ruin in their desire. For a cloud of error prevents their seeing what is best. Look, here is a good example: the Trojans now desire

Troilus and Criseyde

the return of Antenor, who finally brought them to destruction. He later became a traitor to Troy; alas, he was too soon delivered! O foolish world, observe your discretion! Criseyde, who never harmed the Trojans, can no longer remain in bliss, but Antenor will come home and she must leave; so decreed the Trojans.

Though Hector often said "nay," the parliament decided and the president announced that Criseyde would be exchanged for Antenor. And, finally, no matter who opposed this decision, it was in vain. The exchange must and would take place, for the majority of the parliament desired it.

Everyone went away from the assembly. Troilus, still silent, went quickly to his room, alone except for one or two of his men whom he told to leave at once because, he said, he wished to sleep. Then, hastily, he lay down upon his bed. Just as in winter the leaves are one by one blown away until the tree is bare except for bark and branches, so lay Troilus, bereft of all well-being, bound in care's darkness, and almost out of his wits with worry over the exchange of Criseyde. He arose, shut every door and all the windows, and then sat down on the bed, this sorrowful man, as pale and wan as a waxen image. The woe heaped up in his breast began to break forth, and in his madness he behaved as I shall tell you: he writhed like a wild bull which, when pierced to the heart, leaps now here and now there, roaring forth complaints against its coming death.

Just so Troilus rushed about his room, bitterly beating his breast with his fists. Often he crashed his head against the wall and his body against the ground in order to injure himself. His grief caused tears to stream from his two eyes like water

Book Four

from a well. His deep sobs in his sorrow robbed him of speech; he could scarcely ask, "O death, alas, why do you not take me? Cursed be the day that Nature shaped me into a living creature!"

When, after a time, the fury and rage which twisted and crushed his heart began somewhat to subside, he lay down upon his bed to rest. But then his tears came forth at such an increased rate that it was a wonder his body could sustain even half this grief which I now describe. He cried out, "Fortune, alas the time! What have I done? Wherein am I guilty? How can you be so lacking in pity as to beguile me? Is there no grace? Shall I thus be slain? Shall Criseyde thus go away because you wish it? Alas, how can you find it in your heart to be so cruel and unkind to me? Have I not honored you all my life, as you well know, above all the gods? Why will you thus deprive me of all joy?

"O Troilus, what can men now call you but wretch of wretches, fallen from honor into misery, in which I must lament Criseyde, alas, till breath fails me? Alas, Fortune, if my happy life caused displeasure to your foul envy, why did you not kill my father, king of Troy, or my brothers, or me, since I thus complain and cry out, encumbering the world, accomplishing nothing, ever dying but never fully slain? If only Criseyde were left to me, I would not care whither you steered me; yet, alas, you have taken her from me. See, this is always your method: to take from a man that which is most dear to him, thus proving your changeable violence. I am lost; there is no help or defense.

"O true lord, O god, O Love, alas! You know best all my thoughts and my heart. What shall I do in this sorrowful case

Troilus and Criseyde

if I must give up that which I have won with such difficulty? Since you have brought Criseyde and me fully into your grace and have united both our hearts, how can you permit our separation? What shall I do? As long as I endure I shall live in torment and in cruel pain, all alone as I was born, cursing this misfortune or misadventure. I shall never see the rain or sunshine, but shall end my sad life in darkness, and like Oedipus die in distress.

"O weary spirit that twists back and forth, why will you not flee out of the most woebegone body that ever walked the earth? O soul, lurking in this woe, unseat yourself; flee forth from my heart, allowing it to break, and follow always your dear lady Criseyde. Your true place is no longer here.

"O woeful two eyes, since your pleasure was to gaze into the bright eyes of Criseyde, what shall you do except, to my discomfort, accomplish nothing and weep away your sight, since she who was accustomed to illumine you is now extinguished. It is from now on in vain that I possess two eyes, since your inspiration has gone.

"O my Criseyde, sovereign lady of this woeful soul which now cries out, who shall now comfort me in my pain? Alas, no one. But when my heart dies, receive in favor my spirit, which will at once hasten to you and serve you forever. It is of no importance if my body dies.

"O you lovers, who are set in happiness high upon the wheel of Fortune, God grant that you always find love as true as steel, and that you may for a long time live in joy! But when you come to my grave, remember that your comrade rests there, for I also have loved, though I was unworthy.

Book Four

"O old, unwholesome, sinful man—Calchas, I mean—alas, what is the matter with you, that you have become a Greek when you were born a Trojan? O Calchas, who will be my death, accursed for me was the time that you were born! Would to blessed Jove that I could have you where I want you here in Troy!"

A thousand sighs hotter than coals burst from his breast one after the other, mingled with new complaints which fed his woe; as a result his sad tears never ceased. Soon his pains so racked him and he became so weak, that he felt neither joy nor woe, but lay in a trance.

Pandarus, who had heard what every lord and burgess had said in the parliament, and had learned how there was unanimous consent to the exchange of Criseyde for Antenor, went almost out of his mind with grief, and hardly knew what he felt. But in great haste he sought Troilus. A certain knight who guarded Troilus' door at this time let Pandarus enter. Weeping tenderly he went into the darkened room and, as still as a stone, he quietly approached the bed. He was so confused that he did not know what to say, for extreme woe had almost overcome his wit. With his face drawn by grief and his arms folded, he stood before woeful Troilus, looking at his piteous face. Lord, his heart was chilled so often at the sight of his friend's grief that it seemed to him that sympathy for Troilus' distress would kill him. Troilus, the sorrowful one, feeling his friend Pandarus' presence, began to melt like the snow in the sun. At this Pandarus wept with pity as tenderly as Troilus. Thus were these two speechless with sorrow, so that neither could say one word.

Troilus and Criseyde

But at last Troilus, almost dead with pain, burst into a roar and, in a sad voice between his sobs and deep sighs, spoke, "See, Pandarus, I am dead; that is all there is to it. Did you not hear in the parliament that my Criseyde is lost in exchange for Antenor?"

Pandarus, pale as death, answered sorrowfully, "Yes! Would that it were as false as it is true; I heard it and know all about it. O mercy, God, who would have thought this? Who would have thought that in so little time Fortune would have overthrown our joy? In my opinion there is no one in the world who ever saw ruin so strange as this happen by chance or destiny. But who can prophesy all or avoid all? Such is the world! I therefore say that no one should expect to receive constant well-being from Fortune; her gifts are distributed among all. Tell me this: why are you so insane as to grieve as you do? Why do you lie here thus? For you have fulfilled all your desires; surely, that should suffice. Let me, who never experienced in the service of Love a friendly look or glance, weep like this and wail until I die.

"Further, as you yourself well know, this town is full of all sort of ladies. In my opinion, I can easily find one or two in any crowd fairer than twelve like Criseyde. Therefore, cheer up, brother dear! If she is lost, we will find another. Why, God forbid that a man should always find pleasure in one woman and in no other! If one can sing, another can dance well; if one is highly moral, another is light and gay; and if one is attractive, another conducts herself well. Each one is esteemed for her particular virtue; both the heron and the falcon are needed in hawking. Also, as wrote Zeuxis, who was very wise, 'The new love often chases away the old.' A new situation demands a new plan. Think also that you are bound to preserve your life. Such a fire as yours must naturally cool; for since it was but a casual pleasure, some event will drive it from your memory. As surely as day follows night, a new love, work, or another grief, or else seeing the person concerned only seldom, will overcome old affections. In your case, you shall have one of those things to shorten your bitter pains. Her absence will drive her from your heart."

These words were spoken on this occasion by Pandarus to help his friend, lest he die of grief. Obviously, he did not care what dishonorable actions he suggested in order to overcome Troilus' woe. But Troilus, submerged in sorrow, took little heed of Pandarus' intention. The words went in one ear and out the other. At last, however, Troilus answered, "Friend, this cure or treatment which you suggest would be suitable for me if I were a fiend that would betray her who is true to me! I pray God that your advice shall never be accepted. May I die at once on this spot, rather than do as you counsel me! No matter what you say, she whom I serve and who rightfully inhabits my heart will possess me completely until I die. For, Pandarus, since I have promised to be faithful to her, I will not betray her for anyone. I will live and die her man, and never serve another creature. So put aside such statements as being able to find others as fair as she; do not compare her with any merely human creature. Dear Pandarus, in conclusion, I shall not accept your suggestion in this matter.

"Therefore, I beg you hold your peace; you kill me with your talk! You bid me find a new love and let Criseyde go! That does not lie within my power, dear brother; and even

Troilus and Criseyde

if I could I would not do so. If you can play rackets with love—now in, now out, now this one, now that one—then evil will befall her who takes pity on your woe! Also Pandarus, in this matter you behave towards me like that one who comes up to a woebegone person and says, 'Do not think of your pain, and you will not feel it.' You must first transform me into a stone and take away all my feelings before you can so easily do away with my grief. My sorrow may be so deep and lasting that death may well put an end to the life in my breast. But Criseyde shall never leave my soul. When I die I shall go down to Proserpine to dwell in torment, and I shall always complain of how we two were parted.

"You have here advanced the argument that I should feel less pain at Criseyde's leaving because she has been wholly mine and we have lived in comfort and felicity. Why do you babble so, you who once said to me that 'he who is cast from happiness is worse off than he who has never known happiness?' But tell me now, since you think it is so easy to change back and forth in love, why have you not turned your attention to changing from that lady who causes all your grief? Why have you not let her go from your heart? Why do you not love another sweet lady who will comfort you? If you have always had ill fortune in love and yet cannot put it from your heart, how can I, who lived with Criseyde in joy and pleasure as great as that experienced by any living creature, be expected to forget rapidly? O where have you been so long cloistered that you learned to argue so formally and well?

"No, God knows, all your advice is worth nothing; therefore, despite whatever may happen, I will die—that's all. O death, ender of all sorrows, come now to me who calls you so often.

Book Four

For that death is actually kind which, often called, comes and
ends pain. I know well that when my life was happy I would
have paid to avoid your coming, death; but now your coming
will be so sweet to me that I desire nothing so much in the
world. O death, since I am on fire with this sorrow, drown
me at once in tears, or extinguish my heart with your cold
strokes. Since you, unsummoned, slay so many in various
lands night and day, do me this service at my request; you
would do well to rid the world of me, the most woebegone
person there ever was. For it is time for me to die, since I in
no way can be of value to the world."

Tears ran forth from Troilus' eyes like liquid pouring from
a vessel. Pandarus held his tongue and cast his eyes on the
ground. But at last he thought, "Indeed, rather than see my
friend die, I shall say something further to him." Then he
said, "Friend, since you are in such distress and since you
do not care to heed my arguments, why won't you help yourself and put aside all this grief in a manly fashion. You are
ashamed to go steal Criseyde away; so either let her leave
Troy, or keep quiet and stop your foolish behavior. Are you
in Troy and yet without the bravery to take a woman who
loves you and who herself wishes to be with you? Now isn't
that pretty foolishness? Get up at once, stop this weeping,
and know that you are a man. For within this hour I shall
die unless I know she is to remain with us."

Troilus quietly answered him, "Indeed, dear brother, I
have thought of all this very often myself, and of many things
other than you have suggested here. But you shall hear fully
why my grief remains. And when you have given me an audi-
ence, then you can tell all your opinions. First, since Troy

Troilus and Criseyde

experiences all this fighting as the result of the kidnapping of a woman, as you know, I should never be permitted to err similarly or, as things now stand, to do so great a wrong. I should also be blamed by everyone if I went against my father's promise to exchange Criseyde for the benefit of the city. I have also thought that, if she is willing, I might ask my father for her; but it seems to me that this would be only to accuse her unnecessarily, since I know well I cannot buy her thus. Because my father has agreed in so high a place as the parliament to her exchange, he will not repeal his agreement for me.

"Yet most of all I am afraid of upsetting her by violence, if I try such a trick, for to declare my purpose openly would be to slander her name. And I would rather die than defame her; God forbide that her honor were not dearer to me than saving my life! Thus, so far as I can tell, I am lost. Certainly, since I am her knight, I must hold her honor dearer than myself in all events, as any lover should. Consequently, I am torn between desire and reason: desire tells me to go ahead and trouble her; but reason will not agree to it; therefore my heart trembles."

Weeping so that he could not stop, Troilus continued, "Alas, what shall I, wretch, do? Pandarus, I feel my love steadily increasing as my hope becomes less and less. My cause for worry also increases. So, woe to me, why won't my heart break? For in love, there is but little rest."

Pandarus answered, "For all of me, friend, you can do as you like. But if I were so aroused as you, and had your rank, she would go with me even though all this city cried out together against it. I would not care a groat for all such noise! For after men have loudly cried out, then they will whisper;

Book Four

also a wonder never lasts more than nine days in a city. Do not keep on speculating so deeply about reason and courtesy; but help yourself immediately. It is better for others than you two to weep, especially since you are now united. Get up, for by my head, she shall not leave! It is better to be blameworthy to a small extent than to die here like a gnat, without a wound.

"You will do no sin or vice to hold on to her whom you most love. Perhaps she would think you foolish if you allowed her thus to go over to the Greek host. Also remember that Fortune, as you well know, helps the brave man accomplish his purpose, and deserts wretches because of their cowardice. Though your lady would grieve a little, you could later make your peace with her; but as for me, I certainly cannot believe that she would now take it ill. Why then should your heart quake with fear? Think how Paris, who is your brother, got his love; why should you not have yours?

"And Troilus, I am willing to swear one thing: if Criseyde, who is your beloved, loves you now as well as you love her, so help me God she will not take it badly when you try to remedy this mischief. If she desires to leave you, then she is false, and you should love her less. Therefore, take heart, and remember like a knight that each day every law is broken because of love. Now show some of your spirit and your strength. Have mercy on yourself, despite any fears. Do not allow this wretched grief to gnaw into your heart, but like a man stake everything on one cast of the dice; if you die, you will go to heaven a martyr! I myself will aid you in this act, even if I and all my kin should lie together in the street like dead dogs, pierced with many a deep and bloody wound; even so, I

132

Troilus and Criseyde

shall befriend you in any event. But if you wish to die here like a coward, farewell, and the devil take anyone who sympathizes with you!"

Troilus came to life at these words and answered, "Friend, thank you, I agree. But you cannot so incite me, nor can pain so torment me, that for any reason, even though I die, I would make plans to kidnap her, unless she consents."

"That is exactly what I meant all the time," replied Pandarus. "But tell me, have you, who are grieving so, yet determined her reaction?"

"No," answered Troilus.

"Why then," asked Pandarus, "are you pessimistic, when you have not yet found out if she will resent your kidnapping her? Since you have not visited her, you cannot know that fact, unless Jove whispered it in your ear. Now get up at once as if nothing had occurred; wash your face and go to the king, before he wonders what has happened to you. You must subtly deceive him and the others, or he may send for you before you wish it. In brief, dear brother, cheer up, and let me plan this business. For I shall so arrange matters that sometime, somehow, during this night you will have the opportunity to speak to your lady in private. From her words and her manner you will be able at once to hear and to determine her reaction, which in this case will be for the best. Now farewell, on this point I rest my argument."

Swift Rumor, which reports untruths as well as actual facts, had fled on hurried wings throughout all Troy from man to man, and had retold the news that Calchas' beautiful daughter was definitely given by the parliament in exchange for Antenor. As soon as she heard this tale, Criseyde, who cared nothing

Book Four

for her father's deeds or for when he died, earnestly besought Jupiter to curse those who had arranged this exchange. But she dared ask no one the exact situation, for fear she should find that the tales were true. She had her heart and mind so set on Troilus that she could not for all the world unbind her love or cast Troilus from her heart. She wished to be his as long as she lived. Thus she burned both in love and fear, so that she did not know what was best to do.

As is usual everywhere, women make a habit of visiting friends; and soon a group came to call on Criseyde, somewhat enjoying her difficulty and somewhat hoping to encourage her. These women, who lived in the city, sat down and began to tell their lengthy tales, which I shall report. First one said, "I am truly glad for your sake that you will see your father." Then another said, "That is not at all my reaction, for she has been with us too short a time." The third said, "I certainly hope that she will bring about peace between the two armies; may almighty God guide her when she leaves!" These words, along with other feminine comments, Criseyde heard no more than if she had not been present, for, God knows, her mind was on other matters. Although her body sat with those women, her attention was constantly elsewhere; for her soul eagerly sought Troilus. Silent, she steadily thought about him.

The visitors, who believed thus to please her, spun their idle tales about nothing. Such triviality could not comfort her, for all the while she burned with passion other than that which they suspected. Consequently, she felt her heart almost break with grief and boredom in their company. No longer could she restrain the tears which welled up within her, and which

Troilus and Criseyde

indicated the bitter pain of her spirit. She thought of her rapid descent from heaven to this hell, in which she must forego the sight of Troilus, and she sighed sadly. But those fools who sat with her thought she wept and sighed because she must leave them and never be a part of their happy group again. Those who had known her for a long time saw her weeping, considered it natural, and each of them sympathetically wept also. Busily they offered her comfort in matters for which, God knows, she cared little. They thought to distract her with their tales, and they often begged her to be happy. But they accomplished as much toward comforting her as when a man is scratched on the heel to cure a headache! After this foolish visit, they all went to their homes.

Criseyde, sorrowing deeply, went out of the hall into her room and fell on her couch as if dead, intending never to rise again. I shall tell you how she behaved. She tore out her own sunny-colored hair and also often wrung her hands, praying God to take pity on her and send death to cure her troubles. Her face, usually rosy, was now pale, bearing witness to her woes and tenseness. Sobbing, she spoke, "Alas, I, woeful and unlucky wretch born under a cursed constellation, must go from this city and leave my knight. Woe was the light on that day when I first saw him with my two eyes, which brought him and me all this suffering!"

With that, the tears fell down from her eyes like a heavy April shower. She beat her white breast, and begged a thousand times for death, since she must give up the man upon whom her happiness depended. Because of this, she considered herself a lost creature. She said, "What shall he do? What shall I do? How can I live separated from him? O

Book Four

dear heart whom I love so, who shall comfort you in the sorrow which you are in? O father Calchas, all the blame is upon you! Cursed be the day, O mother named Argiva, that you gave birth to me! Why should I continue to live and suffer this grief? How can a fish live out of water? What good is Criseyde separated from Troilus? How can a plant or animal live without its natural nourishment? Therefore, I often state this truth: 'Uprooted, green things must soon die.' I will do thus: since I dare not handle cruel swords and darts, on the very day I leave you, Troilus, unless I earlier die of grief, I shall stop eating and drinking completely until my soul leaves my body. Thereby I shall put myself to death.

"Troilus, all my clothes shall be black to signify, sweetheart, that I who was accustomed to live quietly with you am like one who has left the worldly life. In your absence, until death comes, the convent rules for me shall be sorrow, lament, and abstinence. I bequeath my heart and the sad spirit therein to lament eternally with your spirit, for they shall never be separated. Though we two are parted on earth, yet we shall be as happy together in the field of compassion, called the Elysian Fields, as Orpheus is with his companion Eurydice. Thus, dear heart, I think I must soon be exchanged for Antenor, alas! But what shall you do in this sad situation? How can your tender heart sustain this? My heart, forget your sorrow and pain and forget me also, for, to speak truly, so long as all is well with you, I care not if I die."

How can all the laments she made in her distress ever be read or sung? I do not know, but, as for me, if I tried to describe her grief, my awkward tongue would make it seem less

Troilus and Criseyde

than it was and would childishly ruin her moving lament. Therefore, I pass over it.

Pandarus, who was sent by Troilus to Criseyde—you have heard the plan and have seen that Pandarus was glad to do this for his friend—came secretly to where Criseyde lay in torment and unrest to tell her all about his message. He found that she regarded the matter pessimistically; her face and breast were completely bathed in her salty tears. The long tresses of her sunny hair hung unbraided all about her face. This clearly showed Pandarus that she wished to die a martyr's death. When she saw him she at once hid her tear-wet face in sorrow between her arms. At this, Pandarus was so stricken with grief that he could hardly remain with her; he was completely overcome with pity. If Criseyde had earlier complained sorely, she now lamented a thousand times more grievously.

In her bitter sorrow she said, "Pandarus was the original cause of my many joys which have now turned into cruel woe. Shall I make you, you who first brought me into the service of love, welcome or not, when all ends in this fashion? Does love then end in woe? Yes, or men lie! All worldly joys are the same, it seems to me. The end of bliss is always sorrow. And whoever does not believe that, let him look upon me, a woeful wretch; I hate myself and curse my birth, feeling myself pass from woe to hopelessness. Whoever sees me, sees all sorrows combined—pain, torment, lamentation, woe, and distress! My body does not lack in any suffering—anguish, languor, cruel bitterness, annoyance, pain, fear, fury, and even sickness. I believe that certainly tears rain from heaven because of pity for my sharp and bitter sorrow."

Book Four

"And you, my sister full of discomfort, what do you plan to do about this?" asked Pandarus. "Why do you not have some regard for yourself? Why will you thus torture yourself? Leave all this business and listen carefully to what I shall say. Listen with good intentions to this message which your Troilus sent by me."

Criseyde then turned toward him, making such lament that it was pitiful to hear. "Alas," she said, "what words can you bring? What can my dear heart whom I never expect to see again say to me? Does he wish tears or laments before I leave? I have enough, if he sent for them!"

Her face was just like that of a person lying on his bier. Her face, once the image of Paradise, was altogether changed; the gaiety, the laughter, and every one of the joys people were accustomed to find in her were now fled away. Thus Criseyde lay alone. Two purple rings encircled her eyes, a true sign of her suffering; to look at them was frightening. Consequently, Pandarus could not restrain the tears which poured from his eyes. Nevertheless, as best he could, he delivered the message from Troilus to Criseyde.

He said, "See, niece, I think you have heard how the king and the other lords have considered it best to exchange you for Antenor; this is the cause of all our sorrow and unrest. But the tongue of no mortal man can tell Troilus' disturbance over this fact; he has actually lost his wits because of grief. In fact, he and I have sorrowed so greatly that we are both almost dead. However, through my advice, he finally stopped his weeping somewhat today, and it seems to me that he wishes to spend this night with you in order to devise a remedy for this situation, if any remedy is possible. That is the point

138

of my message, as plain as I can state it. For you, torn and tormented, are in no condition to listen to a long preamble. Therefore you can now send him your answer, and, for the love of God, dear niece, stop your wailing before Troilus arrives!"

"My woe is great," said Criseyde, sighing deeply like one who feels sharp pain, "but still to me his sorrow is much more important. I know I love him better than he loves himself. Alas, does he grieve so for me? Can he lament so piteously on my account? Certainly, his suffering doubles my pain. God knows it is grievous to me to part from him, but it is even harder for me to see the grief which he suffers. I know very well that it will be the end of me; I shall certainly die. However, tell him to come here before the death which thus threatens me drives out the spirit of life that beats in my heart."

Having spoken these words, she fell upon her arms and wept piteously. Pandarus said, "Alas, why do you do this, since you know Troilus will soon be here? Get up quickly so that he will not find you tear-stained, unless you wish to drive him out of his senses. For if he knew how you are acting, he would kill himself, and if I thought that this business would continue, I would prevent his coming here, despite all the wealth which Priam owns. I know what end he would immediately seek. Therefore, I say, stop your grieving, or frankly, he will die. Prepare to lessen his sorrow rather than increase it, dear niece! Be for him a cause for joy rather than grief, and with wisdom you can overcome his sorrow. What use is it to weep until the street is full of tears, in which both of you will drown? A cure is always better than complaint. I mean this: when I bring him here, since you are both wise and of one mind, you can plan to avoid your departure, or to return shortly after you leave. Women are wise on short notice; now let's see how your wits can serve you. I shall not fail to furnish whatever help I can."

"Go, uncle," said Criseyde, "and truly I shall do my best to restrain myself from weeping before him, and to try as hard as possible to gladden him; I shall search my heart for every conceivable way. If any salve can be found for this hurt, it shall certainly not be lacking through my failure."

Pandarus left to seek Troilus. He found him alone in a temple, like a man who cared no longer for life. Troilus prayed feelingly to each of the gods, sadly requesting them to take him soon from this world. For he thought there was no other solution. Briefly, to tell the truth, Troilus that day sank into such despair that he planned to die.

His argument constantly went this way: he said that since he was utterly lost nothing mattered! "For all that comes to men comes by necessity. Thus to be lost is my destiny. Certainly, I know this well: divine Providence has always known that I would lose Criseyde, since God beyond doubt foresees everything, and disposes of things through His orders as they deserve, and as they are predestined to occur. But, nevertheless, whom shall I believe in this matter? For there are many great clerics who prove predestination by numerous arguments; yet some men say there is no predestination and that free will is given to each of us. Oh, woe is me; ancient clerics are so subtle that I do not know which opinion to accept.

"Some men say that if God foresees everything and cannot be deceived, then that which Providence foresaw must happen, even though men swore it should not happen. Therefore, I say that if God has known a thing from eternity before our thought and also our action, then as the clerics maintain, we have no free will. For any other thought or action was not possible, except that which Providence, who cannot ever be deceived, had earlier knowingly seen. If a possibility existed of escaping from God's foreknowledge, then there would be no foreknowledge, but rather only an uncertain opinion and no sure foresight. Certainly it is an abuse to think that God has no more perfect and clearer knowledge than the doubtful opinions of us men. To accuse God of such error is false, foul, and accursed.

"Here is another opinion, held by some of those who have their tops high and smoothly shorn: they say, an event does not come to pass because foreknowledge has earlier known that it will occur; rather, they say that because these events shall come about, Providence wisely and fully foreknows it. Thus, in this opinion, necessity works in the opposite direction, for the necessity is not that whatever is foreseen must occur, but, as they say, that whatever occurs must have been foreseen. In this question I am laboring to determine which thing is the cause of which. Is the foreknowledge of God the sure cause of the necessity with which things come to pass; or is the necessity with which things occur the certain cause of foreknowledge? But I shall not continue trying to determine the order in which these causes stand.

"However, I do know that things foreknown must surely come to pass, even though it is not necessary to consider that the foreknowledge caused the event to occur, no matter whether it is a good or bad event. For if a man is sitting over

Book Four

there in a seat, then necessity surely forces your true opinion when you say or conjecture that he sits. Also, however, the contrary of this is true:—now listen, for I will not take long— if the opinion that he sits is true, then he must by necessity be sitting. Therefore, in either case necessity is present: in him there is certainly the necessity of sitting, and in you the necessity of truth. Thus, there must be necessity in both of you.

"But you may say that the man does not sit as a consequence of the truth of your opinion that he is sitting, but rather that your opinion is true because the man was already sitting there. And I say that, though the truth of your statement comes from his sitting, nevertheless, there is an interchange of necessity between him and you.

"Thus it seems to me beyond question that I may successfully conduct my reasoning about God's providence and the events which do occur in this same fashion. One can clearly see from this reasoning that all things which occur on earth come to pass by necessity. Although it were true that a thing is foreseen because it is sure to come, and not that it comes because it is foreseen, nevertheless, it is certainly necessary that one of the two situations exists. This fact surely suffices to destroy any notion of our having free will. It is ridiculous to say that the occurrence of temporal events causes God's eternal foreknowledge. Truly, it is a false opinion that a coming event causes foreknowledge.

"If I adopted that opinion, I should be thinking that God foresees things to come only because they are to come. Similarly, I would conclude that all the various and sundry events which have come about were the cause of that sovereign

Troilus and Criseyde

Providence which fully foreknows all. In addition, I can say further that just as when I know a thing exists it must by necessity exist, so when I know a thing is coming it must come. Thus the occurrence of things which are known beforehand can in no way be avoided." Then Troilus concluded, "Almighty Jove on high, who knows the truth of all things, take pity on my sorrow and cause my death soon, or bring Criseyde and me out of this distress."

While Troilus spoke in this sad vein and argued the question with himself, Pandarus entered and said, "O mighty God on high, whoever saw a wise man act thus? Why, Troilus, what do you think you are doing? Do you wish to be your own enemy? Criseyde has not yet gone! Why do you wish so to surround yourself in fears that your eyes look dead in your face? Did you not live comfortably for many a year without her? Were you born for her and for no other? Did Nature shape you only to please Criseyde? Stop and remember in your plight that just as chance is present or absent in a dice-game, so pleasure comes and goes in love. The thing I wonder most about is why you now grieve so bitterly when you do not yet know the arrangements for her leaving or whether she can herself avoid it. You have not as yet learned her plans.

"It is soon enough for a man to bend his neck and grieve over the situation when he knows his head will be struck off. Therefore take heed of what I say: I have spoken with her long enough for us to reach an agreement. It seems very clear to me that she has something within her heart with which she can, if I am not mistaken, change all these things that you fear. Therefore, my advice is for you to go to her when night falls and put an end to your sorrow. Blessed Juno, through

Book Four

her great power, shall send her grace to us, I hope. My heart says, 'Certainly Criseyde shall not go away.' Therefore, put your heart at ease for a while and hold to your purpose, for it is the best."

Troilus answered, sighing deeply, "Your advice is good and I shall follow it"; and then he added other things he wished to say. When the proper time arrived, he went quietly to Criseyde, as was his custom. I shall quickly tell you what they did. The truth is that when they first met their hearts were so twisted by pain that neither of them could greet the other; but they embraced and then kissed. They did not know which was the less woebegone, and as I said before, they could not speak a word because of their sobbing and their grief. The sad tears which fell from their eyes were as unnaturally bitter as aloes or gall; sorrowful Myrrha, I find, did not weep such bitter tears through the bark of her tree. There is no heart so hard in this world as not to have pitied the suffering of these two lovers.

But when their two woeful spirits returned to their proper state, and when their woe began at length to lessen somewhat, and their tears to stop as their hearts revived, Criseyde spoke these words to Troilus in a hoarse, broken voice: "O Jove, I die, and I beseech your mercy! Help, Troilus!" With that she bent her head on his breast and lost the power of speech; her sad spirit was on the point of leaving its rightful place. Thus she, once the gayest and fairest of all, now lies pale and sickly.

Troilus stared at her and called her name—she made no answer, acting as if dead; she felt her limbs go cold and her eyes start upward in their sockets. Poor Troilus knew nothing else to do except to kiss her cold mouth frequently. God and he knew whether or not he was woebegone! He arose and placed her at full-length. He could find no sign of life at all in Criseyde, and often cried "Woe is me!" When he saw her lying speechless, he spoke with a sorrowful voice, and from a heart bereft of all bliss, about her departure from this world. After long lamentation for her, he wrung his hands, said the necessary things, and bathed her breast in his salty tears. He then wiped away the tears and piteously prayed for her soul. He said, "O Lord, seated upon your throne, take pity on me also, for I shall soon follow Criseyde!"

She was cold and without feeling, as far as he knew, for he could not find any trace of her breathing. He considered that fact a sure sign that she had left this world. When he could see no least evidence of life, he arranged her limbs in the customary manner when a body is to be placed on a bier. After this, with a stern and determined heart, he drew his sword from his sheath to kill himself, no matter how much he should suffer, so that his soul might follow hers to wherever the judgment of Minos would place it, since Love and cruel Fortune did not desire him to live longer in this world.

Then he disdainfully said, "O cruel Jove, and you, adverse Fortune, the truth of this matter is that you have falsely slain Criseyde; since you can do no worse thing to me, fie on your might and various works! You shall never conquer me in so cowardly a fashion; no death shall separate me from my lady. For I will leave this world, since you have thus slain her, and follow her spirit high or low. No lover shall ever say that Troilus was afraid to die with his lady; certainly I will accompany her. Though you will not permit us to live on earth,

Book Four

permit our souls to be together. Farewell to you, Troy, which I leave in woe, and to you, Priam, and all my brothers, and to you my mother, for I now leave. Atropos, make ready my bier, and you, Criseyde, my dear sweetheart, receive my spirit!" He said all this with the point of his sword at his heart, ready to die.

But, as God willed, Criseyde began to awaken from her swoon and sighed; she muttered, "Troilus."

He asked, "Criseyde, my lady, are you still alive?" and let his sword fall.

"Yes, my heart, thanks be to Venus!" she answered, and sighed deeply.

He began to comfort her as best he could; he took her in his arms and kissed her often, intent on cheering her. As a result, her spirit, which flickered dangerously, returned into her sad heart. At last, as her eyes glanced about, she spied his naked sword and cried aloud with fright. She asked him why he had drawn it. Troilus at once told her his reason and how he would have killed himself with it. At that Criseyde looked fondly upon him, held him tightly in her arms, and said, "O mercy, God, what a deed! Alas, how near we both were to death! If I had not spoken when I fortunately did, would you have killed yourself?"

"Yes, without a doubt," answered Troilus.

"Alas," said Criseyde, "by the same God who created me, I would not long have remained alive after your death, even if I could have been crowned queen of all the lands upon which the sun shines. With this same sword which is here, I would have killed myself. But stop, we have talked enough of death. Let us rise and go at once to bed; there we can discuss our

Book Four

"Atropos, make ready my bier . . .

troubles. For I know by the size of the burning candle that dawn is not far distant."

When they were in her bed, enfolded in each other's arms, it was not like previous nights they had spent together. For each looked piteously at the other, as if their happiness were completely lost, and constantly bewailed the day that they were born.

At last the woeful Criseyde said to Troilus, "See, my heart, you well know that if a person laments his situation and does not try to help it, the only result is a foolish increase of his suffering. Since we two are here together in order to find a remedy for our distress, it is time we began. I am a woman, as you know very well, and in feminine fashion I suddenly have an idea which I shall tell to you while it is still fresh. It seems to me that neither of us needs to be even half so woeful as we are. For we have subtlety enough to straighten out whatever is wrong and to put an end to our sadness. As far as I know, the grief we now experience results from nothing else except the necessity for our parting. When all is considered, there is nothing else wrong. What remedy is there for this grief except for us to plan to meet again in the near future? There is the whole answer, my dear sweetheart. Now, I have no doubt at all but that I can arrange to return soon after I leave. Surely, within a week or two I shall be back here again. In a few words I shall show you many reasons why everything will be all right. I shall not make a long sermon of this, for time lost can never be recovered. As best I can I shall go immediately to the main point. For the love of God, forgive me if I say anything which disturbs your peace of mind, for I certainly say it only for the best, protesting always that

Book Four

these words which I speak are only to suggest to you my idea as to the best way we can help ourselves; do not take them otherwise, I pray you. Actually, I shall do whatever you command me—there can be no question about that.

"Now listen: you understand that my departure has been pledged by parliament and, so far as I can see, there is no possibility in the world to oppose that pledge. Since there is no way to alter that fact, let us forget it, and attempt to arrange a better solution. It is true that our separation will distress and annoy us both terribly. However, it is necessary for a servant of Love sometimes to suffer pain if he wishes to have happiness. Since I shall go no farther from Troy than a half a morning's ride, our sorrow should be less. Now there is, as you know, a truce in effect, and I shall not be hidden away in prison; thus, dear heart, you will know all about my situation from day to day. Before the truce is over, I shall be back here. Then the Trojans will have both Antenor and me. Be cheerful now, if you can, and think this way: 'Criseyde has now gone; but what does it matter, she shall soon return!' When, alas? By God, almost at once—before ten days, I dare say. Then we shall be so completely happy in living forever together that all the world will not be able to imagine our bliss.

"I recall that often in situations similar to this we have found it best, in order to conceal our plans, for you and me not to speak together for two weeks, and for me not to watch you passing by. Can you not, then, wait ten days in order to protect my honor in this dilemma? If not, you can certainly endure very little! You also know that all my relatives except my father are here in Troy. The same is true of all that is mine, especially you, dear heart, whom I would not cease to see

148

Troilus and Criseyde

or all the wide world, as wide as it is; otherwise, I hope I never
see Jove's face! Why do you think my father is so eager to see
me, except because of his fear that people in this city despise
me on account of his unhappy act? What does my father
know about the life I lead? If he knew how well I am getting
along in Troy, we would not be troubled by the necessity for
my departure.

"Also, you see men talking of peace more and more each day,
and it is supposed that Queen Helen will be restored to the
Greeks, and that the Greeks will restore that which is ours.
So, even if the talk of peace is the only comforting point, you
can wait with greater peace of mind. For, if peace comes, dear
heart, people will naturally mingle more together and go back
and forth as thick as bees around a hive; every person shall
have liberty to remain where he wishes without opposition.
But even if peace does not come, I must return here. For
where else should I go, or how—worse luck—could I remain
there always frightened among those men at arms? Thus, so
help me God, I cannot see where you have cause for fear.

"Here is another way of looking at matters, if those I mentioned do not suffice for you. My father, as you well know,
is old, and age brings greed. I have just hit upon the trick
with which I shall ensnare him without a net. Listen now, to
see if you agree. See, Troilus, people say it is hard to have the
wolf full and the lamb whole; that is to say, men must often
spend a part to save the remnant. For one can always engrave
with gold upon the heart of a greedy man. I shall explain to
you what I mean.

"I shall take to my father the possessions which I have in
this city, and say that I bring them from a friend or two of his

149

Book Four

for him to keep securely for them, and that his friends fervently pray him to send back in haste for more, because Troy stands in such jeopardy. The promised amount, I shall say, is large—but lest folk take notice, it must be sent by no one but me. I shall also point out to him how many friends I have in the court circle who will mollify the anger of Priam and return my father to favor in case peace comes. So, with one thing and another, sweet, I shall so enchant him with my tales that he will think his soul in heaven.

"Apollo and all the methods of his clerics are not worth three berries. Desire for gold shall so blind my father's perception that I shall easily bring matters to my desired end. If he decides to test the truth of my statements by his astrology, I shall certainly manage to disturb and outwit him, plucking him by the sleeve as he calculates, or to convince him that he has not rightly understood the gods; for the gods speak in ambiguities and, to tell the truth, they tell many lies. I think that fear caused the invention of the idea of gods—so shall I tell him— and that his cowardly heart made him miss the meaning of the gods' text when he fled frightened from Delphi. If I cannot soon convert him and make him do my bidding in a day or two, I swear that I will die."

Truly, I find it written that Criseyde said all this with good intent; her heart was steadfast and kind toward Troilus, and she meant what she said. When she left Troy she almost died with grief, and her firm purpose was to be faithful. Thus write those who knew of her deeds.

Troilus, with open heart and ears, heard all this business explained back and forth, and it actually seemed to him that he was in complete agreement; yet his heart misgave him in the

Troilus and Criseyde

matter of allowing her to go. Finally, he was able to develop sufficient trust in her, and took it for the best. As a result, the great torment of his grief was quieted by hope, and the pleasure of the amorous dance began between them. As the birds in the trees delight in their song among the green leaves when the sun is shining, so the words spoken together by these two delighted them and made their hearts light.

Nevertheless, Troilus could not put Criseyde's imminent departure from his mind. Consequently, he frequently urged her to remain true to her promise, and he said, "Certainly, if you are unkind and do not return to Troy on the appointed day, I shall never have health, honor, or joy. For just as surely as the sun rises in the mornings, unless God leads me, woeful wretch, from this cruel sorrow, I shall kill myself if you delay! Though my death matters little, yet rather than cause me so to suffer, remain here with me, sweetheart. Truly, my lady, the deceits which I have heard you planning are likely to fail completely.

"As men say, 'The bear thinks one thing, but his leader thinks otherwise.' Your father is wise, and, as it is correctly said, 'Men may outrun the wise but not outwit them.' It is very difficult to limp unnoticed before a cripple, for he understands limping. In trickery your father has as many eyes as Argus. Despite his loss of all his possessions, his old cunning still remains with him to such a degree that your feminine tricks will not deceive him, or your pretenses work. That is my great fear. I do not know whether peace shall ever come; but peace or no peace, seriously or jokingly, I know that since Calchas has once been on the side of the Greeks and has therefore completely lost his reputation, he dares not for shame return to Troy. It seems to me only a fantasy to trust in that hope.

Book Four

"You shall also find that your father will urge you to marry. Since he can preach well, he shall so praise and commend some Greek that his words will convince you, or he shall force you to obey him. And Troilus, for whom you will have no pity, shall die without cause in his fidelity! In addition to all this, your father will despise all of us Trojans and say that the city is as good as lost, and that the siege will never be lifted, since the Greeks have so sworn, until we are all slain and our walls torn down. Thus he will frighten you with his words, and I am afraid you will remain with him.

"You shall also see many a lusty knight among the Greeks, full of worthiness, and each of them will strive with heart, wit, and strength to please you, so that you will tire of the crudeness of us poor Trojans, unless pity or steadfastness reminds you of your promise. It is so grievous for me to think of all these things that they will tear my soul from my breast. Beyond question, I cannot hold a high opinion of your leaving, because your father's treachery will ruin us. If you go, you can, as I have already pointed out, consider me as good as dead —that's all. Therefore, with humble, steadfast, and piteous heart, I pray you a thousand times to have mercy. Take pity on the pain of my bitter sorrows and do as I ask: let us two quietly steal away.

"Think what folly it is, when one has the choice, to lose that which is real for that which is only probable. I mean that since we can be together by stealing away before dawn, would there be any sense in our putting your return in doubt by your going to your father? I say that it would be great folly to place that of which we are sure in jeopardy. And to speak in practical fashion of money, we can both take with us enough

152

Troilus and Criseyde

to live in honor and pleasure until we die. That way we can avoid all this doubt, for no matter what other solution you suggest, my heart cannot agree to it. Certainly you have no reason to fear poverty, for I have relatives and friends elsewhere who, though we arrive in our shirts only, would not allow us to lack either gold or equipment, but would honor us as long as we remained there. Let us go at once, for in my opinion that is best, if you will agree."

Criseyde, with a sigh, answered in this fashion: "Certainly, dear heart, we can steal away as you suggest and find such unsuitable new ways of living; but afterwards we shall regret it deeply. So help me God in my greatest need, you are afraid without good cause! On that day when I am false to you, Troilus, my knight, because of respect or fear of my father or any other person, or for rank, joy, or marriage, may Saturn's daughter Juno through her power cause me to dwell eternally in Styx, the pit of hell, as insane as Athamas! I swear to you by every god and goddess in heaven and by every nymph and infernal deity, by great and lesser satyrs and fauns, who are half-gods of the wilderness, that Atropos may cut my thread of life if I am false to you! Now believe me if you will! And you, Simois, flowing like a bright arrow through Troy downward to the sea, bear witness to these words which are here spoken, and on that day when I am unfaithful to Troilus, my own dear one, run backward to your source, and I with body and soul shall sink into hell!

"God forbid that for the sake of any woman you, Troilus, should do as you suggest and run away, leaving all your friends, especially since Troy now has such need of help. Also, take heed of one matter: if this were known, my life and your honor

Book Four

would lie in the balance; God shield us from such misfortune! If it happened that peace later came—as is always the case, accord follows anger—Lord, the sorrow and woe you would shamefully feel at not daring to return to Troy! Before you place your name in such jeopardy, avoid hastiness in this matter, for a hasty man never lacks worries.

"Also, what do you think people all around us would say about this? It is easy to guess that, without doubt, they would say and swear that not love but voluptuous lust and cowardly fear drove you to run away. Thus, dear heart, all your reputation, which now shines so brightly, would be completely lost. Think also of my honor; it now flowers, but would be ruined and stained with filth if I should go away with you in this fashion. Though I lived until the end of time, I could never regain my reputation. Thus I would be lost, and that would be a pity and a sin.

"Therefore, let reason overcome your heat. Men say 'The patient one conquers,' and 'He who will have what he wants must give up what he wants.' Thus make a virtue of necessity through patience, and remember that he who takes no notice of Fortune is always her master. She frightens no one except a coward. Be sure, sweetheart, that before Lucina the bright, sister of Phebus, has passed out of Aries and beyond Leo, I will be back here; there is no doubt of it. I mean, so help me Juno, queen of heaven, that I will see you on the tenth day without fail, unless death prevents me."

"Now, if this is true," said Troilus, "I shall manage to survive ten days, since I see it must be so. But, for the love of God, if it is possible, let us steal quietly away, for my heart tells me constantly that that would be best, if we ever hope to live in peace."

"O mercy, God," cried Criseyde, "what a life this is! Alas, you slay me with grief! I see well from your words that you do not trust me. Now, for the love of the shining Cynthia, do not distrust me this way without cause, for I have pledged you my word to be faithful. Remember that often it is wise to lose time in order to gain time. No, indeed, I am not yet lost to you, though we must spend a day or two apart. Drive the fancies from your mind, trust me, and put aside your grief; otherwise, I swear I will not leave tomorrow. For if you knew how sorely you grieve me, you would stop this. God knows my own spirit weeps when I see you whom I most love weeping, and realize that I must go over to the Greek host. Yes, if it were not for my knowledge that all will be remedied by my return, I would die right here! But I am certainly not so foolish a person but that I can devise a way to return on the day I promised. For who can hold a creature that wishes to go away? Not my father, despite all his quaint tricks! By my thrift, my leaving Troy shall in the future bring happiness to us all.

"I beseech you, therefore, with all my heart, if you care to listen to me, that for your love which is matched by my love, you evidence to me such comfort and good cheer before I leave that you put my heart, which is now at the breaking-point, at rest. In addition, I ask you, my own heart's true sufficiency, not to put me from your thoughts while I am away because of any pleasure, since I am wholly yours. For I am always afraid, because, as men say, love is a thing always full of fear. If you were unfaithful to me—God forbid—there would be no

Book Four

lady in the world so betrayed or woebegone as I, who am completely faithful to you. Surely, if I were otherwise, I would be as good as dead; unless you discover real cause, for God's love do not be so unkind to me!"

To this Troilus answered, "Now God, from whom nothing is hidden, grant me bliss, for since the day I first saw her I was never false to Criseyde, nor shall I ever be while I live. In brief, you can believe me; I know nothing more except that it will be proved by experience."

"Thank you, my good one," said Criseyde. "May blessed Venus prevent my dying before I have opportunity to repay you, Troilus, with the pleasure you deserve. As long as God allows me to keep my wits, I shall conduct myself with as much fidelity as I have found in you, so that honor shall ever reflect upon me. For do not think that your royal rank, or vain pleasure, or your worth in war or tournaments, or pomp, finery, nobility, or even riches made me take pity on your distress; it was your moral virtue founded upon fidelity which caused me first to have pity on you. Also, I was impressed by your gentle heart and manliness, by your opposition to all that seemed evil, such as crudeness and vulgar appetite, and by the control your reason exercised over your passions.

"These things made me yours above every other creature, and so shall I be as long as I live. Neither the passing of years nor the mutability of Fortune can change this fact. May Jupiter, who has power to make the sorrowful glad, grant us the favor of meeting here in this place after ten nights, so that your heart and mine may be rejoined. Now, farewell; it is time for you to rise."

Troilus and Criseyde

After they had long lamented and frequently kissed and embraced, the day began to dawn. Then Troilus dressed himself and, sadly gazing at his lady as one who feels the cold cares of death, he commended himself to her grace. I do not question whether he felt grief, for a man's brain cannot imagine, or his reason consider, or his tongue tell the cruel pains of this sorrowful man, which surpassed every torment down in hell. For when he saw that she could not remain, his soul was torn from his heart. Without further words, he went out of her room.

HERE ENDS BOOK IV

Here Begins Book V

NOW the fatal destiny approached, which Jove controls and commits for execution to you three sisters, the angry Parcae, whereby Criseyde must leave the city and Troilus must dwell in suffering until Lachesis no longer spins out his life-thread.

The gold-tressed Phebus on high had three times melted the snows with his bright beams, and Zephyrus had for as many times brought again the tender green leaves, since the son of Queen Hecuba first began to love Criseyde, whose forced departure on that morning caused him to sorrow greatly.

At nine o'clock Diomede was ready to lead Criseyde to the Greek host. Because of this fact she felt her heart bleed, and she did not know what was best to do. Truly, as one may read in books, there never was a woman so worried or so loath to leave a city. Troilus, completely helpless and like a man who has lost all happiness, awaited his lady, the true blossoming of all his desires and former joys; but farewell now to your happiness, Troilus, for you shall never again see her in Troy! To tell the truth, while Troilus waited in this fashion he manfully hid his grief so that it was scarcely evident in his appearance. But he hovered with others around the gate through which she was to pass, and, though so woebegone that he could hardly sit his horse, he did not lament aloud. He shook with anger, his heart pained him so greatly, when Diomede mounted his horse.

Troilus and Criseyde

Troilus then asked himself, "Alas, why do I endure this foul misery? Why do I not change matters? Would it not be better to die at once than to suffer this way forever? Why do I not cause enough stir before she leaves to occupy both rich and poor? Why do I not bring an uproar to all Troy? Also, why not kill this Diomede? Why not quickly steal her away with the help of one or two of my men? Why do I stand for this? Why do I not help my own cause?"

I shall tell you why he did not do so rash a deed, and why he put aside his ideas: he always had in his heart a kind of fear lest Criseyde, at the mere sign of his intentions, would be killed; see, this was his greatest concern. Otherwise, he certainly would have acted immediately in accord with the ideas I mentioned earlier.

Criseyde, ready to ride out of Troy, sighed deeply and said, "Alas!" But she had to go, whatever happened; therefore, she began the journey in a woeful fashion; there was nothing else for her to do. It is no wonder that she grieved bitterly at having to leave her own sweetheart. Troilus, in a courteous manner and with a hawk on his hand, rode with a large group of other knights for some distance into the valley to accompany her. He would certainly have ridden farther with her, for he was loath to leave, but it was time for him to turn back. At the same moment Antenor arrived from the Greek host, and the Trojans, delighted, welcomed him.

Troilus, though his heart was not light, did his best to keep from weeping, at least, and kissed Antenor in joyful welcome. Then it was fitting that he take his leave of Criseyde. He stared at her piteously, approached nearer to speak to her, and grasped her tenderly by the hand. Lord, she began to weep movingly!

Book Five

He softly whispered to her, "Now hold to the appointed day, and do not cause me to die." Then with a pale face he turned his horse toward Troy, speaking no word to Diomede or to the others.

Diomede, the son of Tydeus, noticed these things, as one who knew more than the mere fundamentals of such business, and he grasped Criseyde's reins tightly. And Troilus rode homeward to Troy. When Diomede saw that all the Trojans had gone, he thought, leading Criseyde by the bridle, "All my labor will not be in vain, if I can help it, for I shall say something to her. At worst it will serve to shorten our journey. I have heard it said at least twenty-four times that 'He is a fool who forgets himself'."

He continued, speculating to himself, "Certainly, if I speak of love or act discourteously, it will come to naught. For surely, if her thoughts are on that one I am thinking of, he cannot so soon be driven from her mind. But I shall find a means to keep her from knowing now what I have in mind."

Diomede, as a man who knew what was for his own good, then began to talk with her of this and that. He asked why she was so troubled and also besought her, if there was anything he could do to make her more comfortable, to command it of him and he would do it. For he swore to her that as a true knight there was nothing that might please her which he would not do all in his power to accomplish, in order to comfort her. He prayed her to put aside her sorrow.

He said, "Certainly we Greeks will be glad to honor you as highly as the Trojans did. I know you think it difficult—it is no wonder, for all this is new to you—to exchange the acquaintance of the Trojans for the folk of Greece whom you never knew. But I hope to God you never find a Greek who is not as steadfast as any Trojan, and also as kind. Because I just swore to be your friend and helper to the best of my ability, and because I have closer acquaintance with you than any of these other strangers, I pray you in the future to demand anything of me, day or night, and no matter how much I am inconvenienced I shall do all I can to please you. I hope you will treat me as your brother and not spurn my friendship. Even though your sorrow is for important matters—I don't know what—I should through deep sympathy be pleased to amend the cause of it. If I cannot redress your wrongs, at least I heartily regret your sadness.

"Though you Trojans have been for many a day and still are angry with us Greeks, nevertheless we both serve the god of Love. Therefore, for the love of God, generous lady, whomsoever you hate, do not be angry with me. Truly, there is no one who could serve you and so little deserve your wrath as I. If we were not so close to the tent of Calchas, who may see us, I would explain my whole purpose to you. But that must be postponed until another day. Give me your hand; I am and shall be as long as I live, so help me God, yours above every other creature.

"I never before said that to any woman, for, as surely as God may cheer my heart, I never before loved another woman in courtly fashion, nor never shall I in the future. For the love of God, do not be my enemy, even though I cannot correctly plead with you, my lady, since I have yet to learn how. Do not wonder, my own fair one, that I so quickly speak of love with you. For I have heard before now of many a man who loved a thing he had never in his life seen. Also, I am not powerful

Book Five

enough to strive against the god of Love; I shall always obey him, and I now beg your mercy. There are so many worthy knights in this place, and you are so fair that every one of them will try his best to win your favor. But if I might have the good fortune for you to call me your servant, no one of the other knights could serve you so faithfully as I will until I die."

Criseyde gave him little answer; she was so oppressed by grief that she had hardly heard his words, except here and there a word or two. It seemed to her that her sad heart would break in two, and, when she spied her father, she almost fell from her horse. Nevertheless, she thanked Diomede for all his effort and his encouragement, and for his offer to her of his friendship. That offer she accepted courteously, and said that she was eager to do what would please him, and that she would trust him who so obviously was trustworthy. Then she dismounted.

Her father took her in his arms and kissed her twenty times, saying, "Welcome, my dear daughter!" She replied that she was glad to see him and stood there, quiet, mild, and gentle. But I shall leave her there with her father, and turn again to Troilus.

Woeful Troilus returned to Troy more sorrowful than ever before, and with a fierce look on his pitiless face. He rapidly dismounted from his horse, entered the palace and, with a swollen heart, went to his room. He took heed of nothing and no one dared speak a word to him. In his room he gave vent to the grief he had earlier confined within himself, and called for death; in his frantic and mad wildness he cursed Jove, Apollo and also Cupid, Ceres, Bacchus and Venus, his

Troilus and Criseyde

birth, himself, his fate, and also nature, and every creature except his lady. He went to bed, where he wallowed and twisted with rage like Ixion in hell. Until almost dawn he remained in this state. But then his heart relaxed a bit, as a result of the tears which welled forth, and he cried piteously for Criseyde and spoke as follows to himself:

"Where is my own lady, dear and beloved? Where is her white breast? Where is it, where? Where are her arms and bright eyes which at this time last night were with me? Now I can weep many a tear in solitude and grasp about, but I find nothing here to embrace except a pillow. What shall I do? When will she return? Alas, I do not know why I allowed her to leave. Would to God I had been slain then! O my heart, Criseyde, my sweet enemy! O my lady, whom I love above all others! You to whom I gave my heart for evermore, see how I die because you do not rescue me! Who looks upon you now, my lodestar? Who sits or stands right now in your presence? Who can now comfort your troubled heart? Now that I am absent, with whom do you confer? Who speaks for me now in my absence? Alas, no one; and that is my heaviest worry! For I know well that you fare as evilly as I. How can I endure this for ten days when I suffer such pain on the first night? What shall she do, sorrowful creature? How can she in her tender nature sustain such grief on my account? Your fresh womanly face shall be pitiful, pale, and sickly because of suffering before you return to me."

When at last he fell asleep, he soon began to groan and to dream of the most terrible things possible. For example, he dreamt that he grieved alone in a horrible place, or that he had fallen into the hands of all his enemies. Then he would spring

Book Five

up suddenly and awake with a start, feeling such a tremor in his breast that his whole body shook with fright. He would then cry out, for he felt as if he fell from a high place; and he would weep, so pitying himself that it was a wonder to hear his fancies. At other times he would comfort himself with all his might, saying it was folly to suffer such fear without cause. But soon his bitter sorrows returned, and anyone would have pitied his grief. Who could properly relate and describe his sorrow, his lament, his suffering, and his pain? Not all the men who have been or are alive. You, reader, may well imagine his state; I am not able to write of such woe. It would be idle for me to labor over a description of it, for my mind is too weary to think.

When Troilus sent for Pandarus the stars were still visible in the sky, though the moon had grown pale, and the horizon had begun to brighten in the east, as it is accustomed to do; then soon afterwards Phebus with his rosy cart arrived for the day's work. Pandarus could not have come to visit Troilus all the day before, even if he had sworn to do so, because he had been with King Priam all day and had not been free to go anywhere. But on this morning he came when Troilus sent for him. For he could easily guess that Troilus, having lain awake all night grieving, wished to tell him of his grief; Pandarus knew that well enough, without any instructions. Therefore, he went straight to Troilus' room and greeted him soberly, sitting down at once on the side of the bed.

"My Pandarus," said Troilus, "I cannot long survive the sorrows I am now suffering. I do not think I shall live until tomorrow. I should therefore like to explain to you the kind of burial I wish, and you can dispose of my possessions any way

164

Troilus and Criseyde

you think best. But I pray you to give close attention to the fire in which my body shall burn to coals, and to the feast and funeral games at my vigils, to see that all goes well. Offer my horse, my sword, and my helmet to Mars; and give my bright shield, dear brother, to Pallas, the shining one. I beg you to conserve the ashes from the burning of my heart in a vessel called an urn, which is made of gold, and give it to my lady whom I serve, for whom I die in this sad fashion. Do me the pleasure of asking her to keep it as a remembrance of me. For I feel sure in my sickness—and I see it clearly from my present and earlier dreams—that I must die. Also the owl, which is called Ascalaphus, has shrieked after me for two nights. God Mercury, guide now my soul, and come for it when you wish!"

Pandarus answered, "Troilus, my dear friend, as I have told you many times, it is folly to grieve thus without cause; that is all I can say. I cannot see any help for a man who will not take advice and counsel; let him dwell with his fancies. But Troilus, I pray you, tell me now whether you believe that in the past any man has loved a woman as deeply as you. Yes, and God knows that from many a worthy knight his lady has gone away for two weeks without his making half as much to-do as you. What is the need for all your worry? You yourself can see that every day certain men are forced to leave their loves or their wives; yes, even though they love them dearly; yet they do not experience such inner strife.

"You know well, my dear brother, that friends cannot always be together. How do those men behave who see their sweethearts wedded and placed in nuptial beds with their friends, as often happens? God knows, they accept it wisely, pleasantly,

Book Five

and quietly, because hope sustains their spirits. Also they can endure a period of suffering; as time hurts them, so it will cure them. You should likewise persevere and allow the time to pass away, while you manage to be happy and cheerful. Ten days is not so long to wait. Since she has promised to return to you, she will not break her promise on anyone's account. Do not fear that she will not find a way to return; I am willing to stake my life on that.

"Send your dreams and all such fancies to the devil, for they arise from your melancholy which punishes you while you sleep. A straw for the significance of dreams; so help me God, I consider them not worth a bean! No man can interpret them correctly. Priests of the temple say that dreams are revelations of the gods; yet they say also that dreams are infernal illusions. And doctors say that dreams arise from physical causes, or from fasting or gluttony. Who truly knows what they signify? Others say that visions come from impressions which one has deep in his mind, and still others think, as they read in books, that men dream naturally in accord with seasons of the year, and that the effect is determined by the moon. But do not believe any dream, for it signifies nothing. Old wives always put faith in dreams and in auguries by birds, for fear of which men think to lose their lives, such as pestilence of ravens or the shrieking of owls. It is both false and wicked to believe in such things. Alas, alas, that such a noble creature as is man should be afraid of such filth!

"Therefore, I beg you with all my heart to spare yourself all this worry. Rise up now without further discussion, and let us consider how we may best pass away the time, and also how gaily we shall live when Criseyde returns, which will be in the

Troilus and Criseyde

near future. So help me God, it is best to do that. Get up, let us talk of the gay life which we have led in Troy and thus pass away the time. Let us also rejoice in the future which will soon bring us happiness. The boredom of these ten days we shall so forget or overcome that it will not in the least depress us. This town is full of many lords, and the truce is still in effect.

"Let us go disport ourselves in a gay group at Sarpedon's, which is not a mile from here. That way you can pass the time pleasantly until the happy day on which you see her who causes all your sorrow. Now get up, my dear brother Troilus, for truly it is not an honor for you to weep and moan in your bed this way. Trust me about one thing—if you lie in bed for one, two, or three days, people will think that you are pretending to be sick because of cowardice, and that you are afraid to get up!"

Troilus replied, "O dear brother, anyone who has suffered grief knows that it is no wonder when a person who feels harm and pain in every cell weeps and is woebegone. I am not at all to blame if I lament and weep constantly, because I have lost all reason for my happiness. But since I must get up, I shall do so as soon as possible. May God to whom I sacrifice my heart send the tenth day soon! For there was never a bird so happy in May as I shall be when she who causes my torment and happiness returns to Troy. Where do you think is the best place in this town for us to go for pleasure?"

"By God, my suggestion is that we ride out and enjoy ourselves at King Sarpedon's," answered Pandarus.

They discussed the ins and outs of this at length, and Troilus at last agreed to rise; then they went to Sarpedon's. As a man

Book Five

who was always honorable and full of largesse, Sarpedon fed them day after day with all the dainties which could be placed on the table, though it cost a great deal. Everyone present said that such hospitality had never before been evident at any feast. Nor was there any pleasing stringed or wind instrument, which so far as anyone knew had ever been heard or spoken of which was not to be found at that feast. Also, never before had so fair a company of ladies been seen in the dance.

But what did all this matter to Troilus, who now because of his grief cared nothing for such things? His piteous heart steadily turned eagerly to Criseyde. His thoughts were always on her, rapidly imagining now this, now that; as a result, no feast could have pleased him. It was a sorrow for him to look at the ladies who were present at the feast, since his lady was absent, and the music brought him no happiness. For she who bore the key to his heart was not there, and he was of the vain opinion that no one should make music.

No hour of the day or night passed but that one could hear Troilus saying, "Oh lovely bright lady, how have you fared since you left? Welcome, indeed, my own dear lady!" But this was only his illusion; Fortune meant to make better sport of him than that! Between noon and the following morning he would read over a hundred times in solitude the old letters she had formerly sent him, conjuring up her face and figure within his heart, and repeating every word they had exchanged. Thus he got through four days, but decided he could stand this no longer.

He said, "Dear brother Pandarus, do you intend for us to remain here until Sarpedon asks us to leave? It would be more polite for us to leave of our own accord. For God's love, let

Troilus and Criseyde

us leave this evening and return home. Truly, I shall stay here no longer."

Pandarus asked, "Did we come here to fetch fire and then run home again? So help me God, I do not know where we could go, to tell the truth, and find anyone more happy to have us than Sarpedon. If we leave here so suddenly, I consider it discourteous, since we said we would spend a week with him. If we now suddenly leave him on the fourth day, he will certainly wonder about it. Let us hold to our original plan. Since you promised him to stay a week, keep your promise; then we can leave."

Through such great efforts Pandarus forced him to remain. At the end of the week they left Sarpedon and went on their way. Troilus said, "Now God send me the grace to find that Criseyde has arrived when I reach home." At that thought he began to sing.

"Yes, a fine chance!" thought Pandarus, and said softly to himself, "God knows, this hot affair will cool before Calchas will send Criseyde to Troilus!" Nevertheless, he joked and teased, and swore that his heart told him that Criseyde would come as soon as possible. When they reached Troilus' palace they dismounted and took their way to his room. Until nightfall they spoke of fair Criseyde; then, when they wished to do so, they went from supper to bed.

At break of day the next morning, Troilus awoke and said piteously to Pandarus, his dear brother, "For the love of God, let us go see the palace of Criseyde. Though we cannot have real gaiety, let us at least look at her palace."

Then, to deceive his servants he found a reason for going into town, and they two went to Criseyde's palace. Lord,

Book Five

poor Troilus was woeful! He thought his sorrowing heart would break in two. When he saw all her doors shut tight, he almost fell from his horse with grief. Also, when he noticed that every window of the palace was closed, he felt his heart chill as if with frost. He became deathly pale, turned away without a word, and rode on so fast that no one could glimpse his face. Then he said, "O desolate palace, O house once called best of houses, O empty and disconsolate palace, O lantern of which the light is extinguished, O palace once day and now night, you ought to fall and I ought to die, because she who was wont to guide us is gone! O palace, once the crown of all houses, illumined with the sun of all bliss; O ring from which the ruby is lost; O cause of woe which once offered solace! Since I can do no better, I should like to kiss your cold doors, if I dared to do so before this crowd. Farewell, shrine from which the saint is gone!"

At this he looked at Pandarus with a changed and piteous countenance. When he found opportunity as they rode along, he told Pandarus his new sorrow and also his old joys, with so sad a mien and so pale a face that anyone would have pitied him.

From then on he rode up and down past all the places in the city where he had earlier experienced joy, and all the memories returned to him. "See, over there I last saw my lady dancing; and in that temple I first saw my dear lady with the bright clear eyes. There I have heard my dear heart laugh lustily, and I saw her once playing happily yonder. There she once said to me, 'Now, sweet one, I pray you love me well.' Over there she looked upon me so fondly that my heart is hers to hold forever. In yonder house on that corner I heard my beloved

Troilus and Criseyde

best lady of all sing in such a melodious voice and so well and clearly that I still seem to hear that blessed sound in my soul. In yonder place my lady first granted me her favor."

Then he thought thus, "O blessed lord Cupid, when I remember all the process whereby you have tormented me on all sides, I think that men might make a book of it like a story. Why do you need to seek a victory over me, since I am yours and wholly at your will? What joy do you find in killing your own followers? Well have you, lord, avenged your wrath on me, you mighty god, dreadful when aggrieved! Now mercy, lord; you know well that I desire your favor above all else, and that I wish to live and die in your faith. For that I ask no reward except one boon: that you quickly send Criseyde back to me. Force her heart to desire to return as much as mine now longs to see her; then I know well that she will not remain long apart from me. Blessed lord, I pray you not to be so cruel towards the Trojan line as was Juno to the royal family of Thebes, as a result of which the Thebans suffered destruction."

Then Troilus went to the gate through which Criseyde had ridden from Troy. There he rode back and forth many times, saying frequently to himself, "Alas, my bliss and comfort rode away! I would to blessed God that I could now see her returning to Troy. I guided her to yonder hill, and there, alas, I took my leave of her. I saw her ride to her father and, as a result, my heart breaks with sorrow. Then at evening I rode homeward, where I now dwell deprived of all pleasure; so shall it be until I see her again in Troy."

He often imagined that he looked defeated, pale and thinner than usual, and that men whispered, "What is the matter with

Book Five

him? Who can guess the true reason for Troilus' great sadness?" All this was caused by his melancholy, which led him to such fancies. At other times he imagined that all the people who passed him by pitied him, and that they would say, "I am very sorry that Troilus will die." Thus, as you have heard, he went through a day or two; his life was such that he was torn between hope and fear. As a result, he liked to set forth in his songs the cause of his sorrow; as best he could, he made a brief song to lighten somewhat his heavy heart. When he was out of sight from every person, he began in a soft voice to sing, as you will hear, of his dear lady who was absent:

THE SONG OF TROILUS

O star, whose light I have completely lost,
With heavy heart I must lament
That always torn by sorrow, night by night,
Toward death I sail, blown by an evil wind;
So then on the tenth night, if I lack
An hour's guidance from your bright beams,
Charybdis will devour my ship and me.

When he had thus sung his song, he soon fell again into his former disease, and every night it was his custom to gaze upon the bright moon and tell her all his sorrow, saying, "If all the world is true, I certainly shall be joyful when you are newly horned. On the morning my dear lady rode from Troy, as a result of which I now suffer, I saw your old horns. Therefore, O bright and shining Lucina, for the love of God, hasten around your sphere! For when your new horns begin to show, then she who brings me bliss will return."

Part Five

His life was such that he was torn between hope and fear

Troilus and Criseyde

The days seemed to Troilus more numerous and the nights longer than usual. He thought that the sun followed a longer path in its course than customarily. He said, "Certainly, I am constantly afraid that Phaeton, the son of Phebus, is alive and drives his father's chariot incorrectly." He walked often upon the walls of the city and stared at the Greek host, saying to himself, "See, my own generous lady is yonder, or perhaps there where the tents are. This air comes from that place, and is so sweet that it cheers my soul. Surely this wind which blows stronger and stronger against my face comes from my lady's deep sad sighs. I can prove that, for in no other place in all of Troy except here do I hear the wind whispering painfully, asking, 'Alas, why did we two part?'"

He continued this way for a long time, until the ninth night had passed. Pandarus was always with him, trying as hard as possible to comfort him and lighten his heart by holding out the hope that on the tenth morning she would come and end all his sorrow.

On the other side of the plain was Criseyde with a few women, among the powerful Greeks. Many times a day she said, "Alas, that I was ever born! My heart may well desire death, for I have now lived too long. Alas, I cannot help matters, for they are now worse than I ever expected. My father will by no means allow me to return; I can in no way convince him. If I do not keep my promise, my Troilus in his heart will judge me false, and it will seem so. Thus shall I be blamed on every side. Woe the time that I was born! If I jeopardize myself by stealing away at night, and then it happens that I am caught, I shall be considered a spy. Or, otherwise,—and I fear this most of all—if I fall into the hands

Book Five

of some wretch I am lost, though my heart is faithful. Now mighty God, You take pity on my sorrow!"

Her bright face grew pale and her body thin, for when she dared she stood all day gazing at that city where she was born and had always lived; and all night she lay weeping. Thus in despair, beyond all hope, this woeful creature led her life. Many times a day she sighed with distress and called up memories of Troilus' great worth and all his noble speeches since the day she first began to love him. At this her sad heart caught fire, for her memories increased her longing. No one in the world has so cruel a heart that he would not have wept at her suffering, if he had heard her lament and grieve day and night. She had no need to borrow tears! The worst of her situation was that she dared tell no one of her sorrow. Ruefully she looked at Troy with its high towers and its buildings.

"Alas," she said, "the pleasure and joy which I often experienced within those walls have now turned to bitterness. O Troilus, what are you doing now? Are you still thinking of Criseyde? Alas, that I did not accept your suggestion and flee with you as you wished. Then I would not be sighing now half so sorely. Who could have said that I did wrong to run away with such a man as Troilus? But the remedy comes all too late when men are carrying the corpse to the grave. It is now too late to speak of such matters. Also, Prudence, I always lacked one of your three eyes, even before I came here. I could easily remember the time past, and the present also it was not difficult for me to see, but future events I could not see until I was caught in the trap; that causes my present suffering.

174

Troilus and Criseyde

"Nevertheless, come what may, tomorrow night I shall somehow, by east or west, slip away from this army, and go with Troilus wherever he wishes. I will hold to this purpose, for it is the best. The jangling of wicked tongues does not matter; for wretches always envy true love. Whoever takes heed of every word or guides himself by the opinion of everyone, surely will not thrive. That which is blamed by some is commended by others. As for me, among all such diverse opinions, I find felicity sufficient. Therefore, without any further discussion, I will go to Troy."

But, God knows, before two months had passed Criseyde was a long way from that purpose! For both Troilus and Troy will easily slide from her heart, and she will decide to remain with the Greeks.

This Diomede, whom I mentioned earlier, spent all his time debating with himself about what trick he might best use in order to bring Criseyde's heart into his net as quickly as possible. He never lost sight of this purpose; to catch her, he laid out his hook and line. Nevertheless, he realized clearly that she was not without a lover in Troy, for he had not once seen her laugh or jest since he had brought her to the Greeks. He did not know how best to win her heart. "But it does not grieve me to try," he thought; "he who tries nothing, wins nothing."

One night Diomede said to himself, "Now am I not a fool to try to win her when I know she grieves over another man? I may well regret it, for it will not profit me. Wise men say in books, 'A man should not woo a lady who is sad.' But whoever could win such a flower from him for whom she grieves night and day, he might well claim to be a conqueror." Then he at

Book Five

once decided, for he was always bold, "Let what will happen happen; I will seek her heart though I should die for it. I have nothing to lose but words."

Diomede, we learn from the books, was determined and bold in his aims. He had a stern voice and mighty limbs, he was hardy and headstrong, sturdy and chivalrous in deeds like his father Tydeus. And some say that he had a loose tongue. He was heir to Calydon and Argos.

Criseyde was of average stature; there was no fairer creature in form, and also manner. It was often her custom to go with her bright hair hanging down her back, bound only with a thread of gold. Except that her eyebrows came together, there was no flaw in her beauty, as far as I can tell. But to speak of her bright eyes—those who saw her actually wrote that Paradise stood formed in them. Always within her, love strove with her rich beauty to see which was greater. She was quiet, simple, and wise, as well-bred as one could be, able in her general speech, charitable, stately, happy, and generous. Pity was never lacking in her. She was tender hearted and unstable in her affections; but, truly, I cannot tell her age.

Troilus was tall and built proportionately so well that nature could not have bettered him physically. He was young, lusty, strong, and brave as a lion, true as steel in every way, and one of the best endowed with virtues of all creatures who live or shall live in this world. Certainly it is found in the story that Troilus was never second to anyone in his time in the feats of arms befitting a knight. Though a giant might have greater strength than he, his heart was equal to the best and greatest in any deed he wished to do.

176

Troilus and Criseyde

But to continue with Diomede—it happened that on the tenth day after Criseyde had left Troy, Diomede, fresh as a tree in May, came to Calchas' tent, pretending to have business with Calchas. I shall soon tell you what he had in mind. Briefly, Criseyde welcomed him and sat him down beside her. It was easy enough to get him to stay! Shortly after that, servants brought out spices and wine. Diomede and Criseyde spoke together of this and that, as friends do. You shall hear some of their talk.

He first began to speak of the war between the Greeks and the Trojans. He asked her to tell him her opinion of the siege. From that request he moved on to ask her if she thought the Greek manners and customs strange, and why her father waited so long to marry her to some worthy knight. Criseyde, who suffered deeply because of her love for Troilus, her own knight, answered him with all her skill, but she seemed to miss the purpose of his questions.

Nevertheless, Diomede encouraged himself and said, "If I have observed you correctly, my lady Criseyde, it seems to me that I have never seen you except in sorrow since I first laid hand on your bridle, on the morning that you left Troy. I cannot guess the cause, unless you grieve because of love for some Trojan. It would disappoint me sorely for you to spill a quarter of a tear or piteously torment yourself on account of anyone remaining in Troy. For, doubtless, it is not worth your while. The folk of Troy, as everyone knows and as you yourself see, are in prison. Not one of them shall escape alive from there, for all the gold between the sun and the sea. Trust and understand me: not one of them shall through mercy be left alive, even if he were lord of ten worlds! Such revenge

Book Five

shall be taken on them before we leave here, because of the theft of Helen, that the Manes, gods of torment, shall be afraid that the Greeks will punish even them. Until the end of the world, men shall fear to kidnap any queen, so cruel will be our revenge on the Trojans. Unless Calchas has misled us with ambiguities, that is, with sly double talk, such as people call a word with two meanings, you shall know by seeing all this with your own eyes that I do not lie. And it will happen soon—you won't believe how soon. Now take heed, for it will surely come to pass.

"Why, do you think your wise father would have exchanged Antenor for you if he were not convinced the city will be destroyed? No, as I hope to prosper! He knew full well that not one Trojan shall escape, and because of his great fear he dared not allow you to remain there longer. What more do you wish, lovely dear lady? Put Troy and Trojan from your heart! Drive out your bitterness and become happy, recalling to your face the beauty which your salty tears have so marred. For Troy has now come into such jeopardy that there is no remedy which will save it. Remember that among the Greeks you could find before nightfall a lover more perfect, kinder, and better able to serve you than any Trojan. If you but agree, my bright lady, I myself shall be he who serves you—yes, rather than be lord of twelve Greeces!"

With these words he began to turn red; his voice trembled slightly as he spoke; he twisted his head a bit to the side, and sat silent for a while. Afterward he recovered, threw a glance at her soberly, and said, "I am, though it is no great claim, as much a gentleman as any man in Troy. For if my father Tydeus had lived, I would have been ere this, Criseyde, king

Troilus and Criseyde

of Calydon and Argos; and so I still hope to be! But he was slain at Thebes—alas, the greater harm—unfortunately too soon for Polynices and many others. However, my heart, since I am your man—and you are the first from whom I ever sought favor—I am and ever shall be while I live eager to serve you as best I may. Therefore, before I leave this place, grant me the chance to tell you tomorrow at greater leisure of my feelings."

Why should I repeat more of Diomede's words? He spoke enough, for one day at least. His talk had some results, for Crisyede agreed to his request that she speak with him the next day, so long as he would not mention love. She spoke to him, as you will hear, as one who had her heart so firmly set on Troilus that no one could change it.

Rather haughtily she said, "Diomede, I love that place where I was born. May Jove in his kindness deliver it from all its present troubles! God, use your power to cause it to fare well! I know full well that the Greeks wish to vent their wrath on Troy if possible. But it shall not happen as you predict, God willing. Further, I know my father is wise and careful; I am the more beholden to him because he has, as you said, bought me so dearly. I know also that the Greeks are of high nobility, but surely one can find folk in Troy as noble, skillful, perfect, and kind as any between the Orcades and India. I believe that you could serve your lady well and merit her thanks. But, to speak of love, I had a lord to whom I was married and who wholly possessed my heart, until he died. There is not, so help me Pallas, any other love in my heart, nor never was there. I have heard frequently that you are of a high and noble family, and that causes me to wonder greatly at your

Book Five

mocking any woman as you have me. God knows, love and I are far apart! I am surely more inclined to lament and grieve until I die.

"I cannot say what I shall do in the future, but truly I now have no desire for frivolity. My heart is now in mourning, and you are busy fighting day by day. Perhaps in the future, when you have won the city and when I see that which I never expected to see, it may happen that I shall do that which I never expected to do. These words should suffice for your answer. Tomorrow I shall gladly talk with you, if you avoid any discussion of love. You may come here again whenever you wish. Before you leave I will say this much to you: so help me Pallas of the shining hair, if ever I take pity on any Greek, I promise it shall be you! Thus, I do not say that I will love you, nor do I say that I will not. My last word is that, by God above, I mean well." With that she cast her eyes down, sighed, and said, "O town of Troy, I pray to God that I may see you in peace and quiet; otherwise my heart will burst!"

But, briefly, Diomede actually began again to press forward and to beg her mercy. Later, to tell the truth, he took her glove, which he was happy to have. Finally, when evening came and all went well, he rose and took his leave.

Bright Venus, always following Phebus, showed the path by which the sun had set; and Cynthia was urging her chariot-horses to whirl from the Lion if possible; the Zodiac showed his bright candles, when Criseyde went to bed in her father's white tent, constantly turning up and down in her mind the words of hasty Diomede, together with his high rank, the peril of Troy, and her need of a friend's help in her unprotected

Troilus and Criseyde

situation. Thus the idea was born which, to tell the truth, later caused her to decide to remain with the Greeks.

Morning arrived and, to speak rightly, Diomede came to see Criseyde. Briefly, for fear you will interrupt my story, I say only that he spoke so well in his own behalf that he overcame her deep sorrow. Finally, all her grief was truly driven out because of him. The story tells us that after this she gave back to him the fine bay horse which he had once won from Troilus, and also that she gave him a brooch which Troilus had given her—there was little need for her to do that. Also, the better to heal Diomede's suffering, she gave him a token from her sleeve. I find elsewhere in the stories that when Diomede was wounded in the body by Troilus, she wept many a tear at the sight of his deep, bleeding wounds, and that she carefully nursed him. And men say—I don't know—that in order to end his sorrow she gave him her heart. But, actually, the story tells us that no woman ever felt greater woe than she when she deceived Troilus.

"Alas, now my reputation for fidelity in love is completely gone forever," she said. "For I have deceived one of the noblest and worthiest of knights who ever lived. Alas, until the end of the world no good word will be written or sung about me; for I will be ruined in the books. Oh, I shall be rolled on many a tongue! Throughout the world my bell shall be sounded! And women will hate me most of all; alas, that such a thing should happen to me! They will say that I have done them dishonor to the full extent of my ability. Although I am not the first to do amiss, what help is that in removing my blame? Since I see no better way, and since it is too late for regrets, I will always be true to Diomede. But Troilus,

Book Five

since I can do no better and since you and I must remain apart, I pray God to treat you kindly, as the most truly noble servant in love that I ever saw, and as the best guardian of his lady's honor." With these words she burst into tears.

"Certainly I shall never hate you"; she continued, "you shall always have a friend's love from me and my good word, even if I should live forever. Truly, I should regret seeing you in adversity, and I know well that I leave you with no guilt on your part. But all shall pass; thus I take my leave of you."

No author actually states, I think, how long a time passed before she forsook Troilus for Diomede. Let every man now examine his books; he shall certainly find no definite period stated. Though Diomede began to woo her early, he had more to do before he won her. But I do not wish to chide this poor woman more than the story does. Her name, alas, is so widely dishonored that it should be sufficient punishment for her guilt. If I could in any way excuse her—for she really regretted her infidelity—I would certainly do so out of pity.

Troilus, as I mentioned earlier, lived through the days as best he could. But his heart often turned from hot to cold, especially on that ninth night which preceded the morning of Criseyde's promised return. God knows, he had very little rest that night, for he had no desire to sleep. The laurel-crowned Phebus began in his steadily rising course to warm the waves of the eastern sea, and Nysus' daughter, the lark, began a new song when Troilus sent for Pandarus. They strolled along the walls of the city to see whether they could catch sight of Criseyde. They watched all who entered until noon. As each new person approached in the distance, they said it was Criseyde, until they saw that it was not. First

Troilus and Criseyde

Troilus' heart was heavy, then it grew light. Thus, staring at nothing, Troilus and Pandarus stood there in a mockery.

Troilus said then to Pandarus, "For all I can tell, Criseyde surely did not enter this city before noon. Probably she has enough to do in persuading her father, I think. Her old father is making her dine with him before she leaves, God curse him!"

Pandarus answered, "That may very well be. Therefore let us dine, I pray you, and afterwards you can return here." They went home without more talk, and later returned. But they must look a long time before they find what they are seeking! Fortune has planned a joke on both of them.

Troilus said, "I now see that she has tarried so long with her old father that it will be almost evening before she arrives. Come on, I will go as far as the gate. The porters are always stupid, and I will make them keep the gate open, so that she can enter even if she comes late."

The day quickly faded and then night came, but Criseyde still did not return to Troilus. He looked along the hedges, the trees, and the groves, placing his head far over the wall, but all in vain. Finally he turned and said, "By God, I see now what she intends, Pandarus! My grief was about to start again. Without doubt, this lady can take care of herself: I know she means to ride secretly. By my head, I commend her wisdom. She does not want people foolishly staring at her when she arrives; she plans to slip quietly into town by night. Do not think, dear brother, that we shall have to wait long. We certainly have nothing else to do. Now, Pandarus, will you believe me? You have my word that I see her! Yonder she is! Raise your eyes, man! Don't you see her?"

Book Five

Pandarus answered, "No, as I hope to prosper! By God, you are all wrong. What did you say? Where is she? I see nothing there but a cart."

"Alas, you are right," said Troilus. "But it cannot be all for naught that I now rejoice in my heart. It is because of a hint about some approaching pleasant event. I do not know why, but never since I was born have I felt such comfort as now. She will come tonight; I would lay my life on that!"

Pandarus replied, "It may well be," and held within him all his doubting speeches. But he laughed to himself and soberly thought, "All that you wait for here will come only in your imagination. Yes, farewell to all the snows of yesteryear!"

The guard at the gates began to summon all the folk who were outside the wall, bidding them drive their cattle inside or else stay out all night. Late at night, Troilus rode homeward, blinded with tears, for he saw there was no need to wait longer. Nevertheless, he encouraged himself with the thought that he had miscounted the days, and said, "I have misunderstood everything. For on the last night I saw Criseyde, she said 'I shall be here if I can, dear sweetheart, before the moon, now in the Ram, shall pass out of the Lion.' According to that, she can still keep her promise."

Next morning he went again to the gate and took many a turn, up and down, east and west, upon the walls. But all was in vain; his hope always misled him. Therefore at night, in sorrow and with deep sighs, he went straight home. His hopes had completely gone. He had no further straws at which to catch, and his suffering was so sharp and strong that it seemed to him that his heart bled with the pain. For when

Troilus and Criseyde

he saw that she had remained so long away, he did not know what to make of it; she had broken her promise to him.

During the third, fourth, fifth and sixth days, after the ten days I spoke about, Troilus' spirit lay between hope and fear, for he still to some extent put faith in Criseyde's former promises. But when he saw that she had broken faith, he knew no other remedy than to prepare himself for death. The wicked spirit which people call insane jealousy crept into him, despite his sadness. As a result, since he was soon to die, he would neither eat nor drink and fled in his melancholy from all his companions: this was the way of life he followed. He was so despondent that he was scarcely recognizable by anyone wherever he went; so lean, pale, wan, and feeble was he that he had to walk with a staff. He constantly tormented himself with his anger. If anyone asked him why he suffered, he replied that he had heart trouble. Priam, his mother, his brothers, and his sisters often asked him why he was so sorrowful and what it was that troubled him, but all in vain; he would not reveal the true cause, but said that he felt a grievous malady about his heart and was eager to die.

So one day he lay down to sleep and it happened that in his sleep it seemed to him that he walked in a deep forest to lament for love of her who caused his suffering. As he wandered up and down the forest, in his dream he saw a boar with huge tusks, sleeping in the warmth of the bright sun. By this boar lay his fair lady, Criseyde, tightly enfolded in his arms and frequently kissing him.

In anguish and sorrow at this sight, Troilus awakened and cried out loudly to Pandarus, "O Pandarus, now I know all. I am as good as dead; there is no other solution. My fair lady,

Book Five

Criseyde, whom I trusted above all others, has betrayed me. She has bestowed her heart elsewhere. The blessed gods, through their great might, have revealed that fact in my dream, in which I have beheld Criseyde thus"—and he told Pandarus the whole story.

"O my Criseyde, alas," he continued, "what just cause have you to use your subtlety, desire, beauty, cunning, and anger against me? What guilt or harmful deed on my part has bereft me of your favor? O trust, O faith, O deep assurance, who has stolen from me my Criseyde, all my happiness? Alas, why did I permit you to go away from here? As a result, I am almost out of my mind. Whose sworn promises can now be believed? God knows that I thought, my lady Criseyde, every word you spoke was gospel. But who can better deceive, if he wishes, than the man in whom people trust most fully? Alas, what shall I do, Pandarus? I now feel such bitter new pain because there is no remedy in this matter, that it would be better for me to kill myself with my own two hands than to lament forever. For by death my woe will be ended, while every day I live I torment myself."

Pandarus answered, "Alas that I was ever born! Have I not told you before now that dreams are full of deception? Why? Because folks interpret them wrongly. How dare you say because of a dream that your lady is false, just because you fear that? Put aside such a thought. You cannot interpret dreams. Perhaps the boar of which you dreamt may signify her father, who is old and gray, lying in the sun at the point of death, for which she weeps in sorrow and kisses him as he lies on the ground. That is the correct explanation of your dream."

Troilus and Criseyde

"What can I then do," asked Troilus, "in order to learn any part of the truth in this matter?"

"Now you speak wisely," replied Pandarus. "My advice is for you, who can write well, to compose a letter to her at once, through which you will manage to learn the truth about that of which you are now in doubt. Here is my reason: I dare say that if she is unfaithful to you, I can not believe that she will send you a letter in reply. But if she replies, you will know immediately whether or not she is free to return. Or perhaps, if she is forcibly detained, in some way she will state the reason. You and she have not exchanged letters since her departure. I dare say that she may have sufficient reason for her action so that you will agree that she does best for you two by remaining there. Now write to her, and soon you will know the whole truth. That is the only thing to do."

These two lords soon agreed on this plan. Troilus at once sat down and debated with himself how he might best describe his woe. Finally, he wrote as follows, as you may see, to his own lady, Criseyde:

TROILUS' LETTER

Blossoming flower, to whom I have belonged and always shall belong—without any division of my love and with all my heart, body, life, will, and thought—I, a woeful one, in every humble manner which tongue can tell or mind devise, recommend myself to your noble favor, as fully as matter fills space.

May it please you to recall, sweetheart, that which you well know—how long the time since you departed, when you left me suffering bitter pains, from which I have in no

Book Five

way recovered; rather, from day to day I grow worse and must continue to do so at your discretion, my well of happiness and sorrow. Therefore, I am writing to you with a fearful true heart, as one driven to this extremity by grief, to proclaim my woe which increases hourly, and to lament as I dare or am able. If my writing is in any way blotted, you may know that it results from the desire of the tears which run from my eyes to speak, if they were able, and to lament.

I first beg you not to think your clear eyes defiled by examining this letter, and, in addition, that you, my dear lady, will deign to read. If there is anything amiss in the letter, forgive it, sweetheart, as resulting from my great worries which have overcome my wits. If any lover has the right to dare complain piteously to his lady, then I think that I ought to be that man, considering that you have tarried two months when you promised faithfully to return in ten days. Yet in two months you still have not returned. But since I must needs like that which pleases you, I dare not complain further; I simply write to you, amid my deep sorrowful sighs, to tell of my great suffering and in the desire to know more fully day by day how you fare and what you do, if you care to tell me. May God add to your welfare and health so that your honor will increase in degree each day without end. You have the ability to find a solution, my generous lady—I hope to God it will be so—whereby you can soon take pity on me, for I am fully faithful to you in all ways.

If you wish to know the situation of one whose woes defy description, I can only say that I, filled with cares,

Troilus and Criseyde

was alive at the writing of this letter, though ready to release my woeful spirit which I retain until I learn the import of your reply. My two eyes with which I search in vain have become wells of sorrowful salty tears; my song has become a lament for my adversity; my good has turned to evil; my comfort has turned into a hell; and my joy is now woe. I can say nothing further, except that my every joy and pleasure is reversed; therefore I curse my own life. You can right all these troubles by returning home to Troy, and increase my happiness a thousandfold above that which I formerly knew. For never was there a heart so happy to live as mine will be as soon as I see you. If pity does not at all move you, then remember your promise.

If I am so guilty as to deserve death, or if you do not wish ever to see me again, I beg you, as a reward for my service to you, generous lady of my heart, to write that fact to me, for the love of God, my lodestar, so that I may end all my troubles by death. If you remain with the Greeks for another reason, a statement of that reason in your reply will comfort me. For though your absence is a hell for me, I shall patiently restrain my woe and gain hope from your letter. Now write, sweet, and put an end to my laments; deliver me from pain with either hope or death. I am sure, my own dear true heart, that when you next see me you will not recognize me, so have I lost my health and color. Certainly, my heart so thirsts to see your beauty, my lady, that I can scarcely hold on to life.

I shall say no more, though I have much more to tell you. But no matter whether you cause me to live or die,

Book Five

I pray God to send you good days! Farewell, good fair one, you who can command life or death for me. To your fidelity I recommend myself; I am in such a position that unless you give me happiness I can have no happiness. In you lies the power, when you wish to use it, to decide the day on which I shall be buried. With you lies my life and the ability to save me from the disease of sorrow. And now farewell, my own sweetheart!

Your Troilus

This letter was sent to Criseyde, whose answer was in effect as follows: she replied in piteous vein and said that as soon as possible she would certainly return and amend all that was amiss. In conclusion she said that she would come, but that she did not know exactly when. In her letter she made wonderful promises and swore that she loved Troilus best. He found these statements to be without foundation. Troilus, you can now go east or west, and whistle up a tree, if you wish! Thus goes the world! God shield us from misfortune and advance everyone who keeps faith!

Troilus' woe grew by night and day because of Criseyde's tarrying. His hopes and strength lessened and he took to his bed. He would not eat, drink, sleep, or speak a word, imagining always that Criseyde was unfaithful. As a result, he almost lost his wits. He could not put the dream which I mentioned earlier out of his mind. For he was sure that he had lost his lady, that Jove in his providence had made her faithlessness and his misfortune clear to him in sleep, and that the boar was meant to be symbolic. Therefore he sent for his sister the Sibyl, whom everyone called Cassandra, and he told her

Troilus and Criseyde

his complete dream, asking that she end his doubts concerning the large boar with the strong tusks.

In a little while, Cassandra interpreted his dream to him. She smiled and said, "Dear brother, if you wish to know the full meaning of this dream, you must first hear a few ancient tales which are connected with your dream and which show how Fortune in the past overthrew certain lords. Through these studies, which can be read in books, you will quickly know who the boar is and to what family he belongs. Diana, angry because the Greeks would not make sacrifices to her or burn incense upon her fire, and because they despised her, took revenge in an amazingly cruel fashion. She caused a boar as large as an ox to eat up all their grain and vineyards. The whole country was aroused to kill this boar. Among those who came to see the boar there was one of the most highly praised maidens in the world. Meleager, king of that country, so loved this beautiful maiden that he killed the boar to show his manhood, and sent the head to the maiden. Because of this, as old books tell us, great strife and hatred arose. Tydeus is descended straight from this lord, or else the old books lie. But I shall not tell you how Meleager was brought to death through his mother—for that would take too long."

Then Cassandra told how Tydeus went to the strong city of Thebes to claim the kingship for his friend Polynices, whose brother Eteocles wrongfully held it. She told all this at length and in detail, and how Haemonides escaped when Tydeus killed fifty strong knights. She recited all the prophecies by heart and how the seven kings lay seige to the city with their army. She also told him of the holy serpent, the well, the Furies, the funeral-games at Archemorus' burial, Amphiaraus'

Book Five

fall through the ground, the slaying of Tydeus, lord of the Argives, Hippomedon's quick drowning, Parthenopeus' death from wounds, and proud Capaneus' being killed by a thunderbolt.

In addition she related how the two brothers, Polynices and Eteocles, slew each other in a skirmish, how sorely the Argives wept and grieved, and how the town was burned. Thus she came down from the ancient stories to Diomede. She said, "This boar symbolizes Diomede, son of Tydeus, who is descended from Meleager who killed the boar. And wherever your lady is, certainly she has exchanged hearts with Diomede. Weep or not, as you like; for beyond question, Diomede is in and you are out!"

"You sorceress, you do not speak truth," cried Troilus, "with all your pretended prophecy! You think you are a great seeress. Now look at this fanciful fool who tries to slander ladies! Away! May Jove send you woe! You will probably be proved false before tomorrow. You might as well slander Alcestis who, unless men lie, was the best and kindest of creatures who ever lived. For when her husband's life was in jeopardy, dependent upon her death, she chose to die at once in his place and go to hell, as the books relate."

Cassandra left, and Troilus' anger at her speech drove the woe from his heart. Suddenly he jumped up from his bed, as if a physician had cured him completely. Day by day he sought and inquired diligently for the truth in this matter. Thus he pursued his destiny.

Fortune, to whom Jove's providence has assigned the responsibility for change in such things as rulership and death, began to pull away each day the bright feathers of Troy, until

Troilus and Criseyde

the city was left bare of happiness. During this period, the end of Hector's life was fast approaching. Fate wished to release his soul from his body, and had found a way to accomplish that. It was to no avail for him to strive against Fate. He went to fight one day, on which, alas, he lost his life. It seems to me that every man who practices arms should bewail the death of this noble knight. For when Hector wounded a king through the stomach, Achilles cut through his armor and body. Thus this worthy knight was killed.

Such woe was made for his death, the old books say, that the tongue cannot describe it. Especially moving was the grief of Troilus, next after Hector in knightly prowess. What with sorrow, love, and doubt, Troilus was so woebegone that he often wished his heart would break. Nevertheless, though he despaired and steadily doubted his lady's fidelity, his heart repeatedly turned to her. As is customary with lovers, he strove constantly to regain the fair Criseyde. In his heart he excused her completely and blamed Calchas for her tarrying.

Many times Troilus thought to disguise himself as a pilgrim so that he could go visit her. But he could not hope to remain unrecognized among wise folk, nor could he find sufficient excuse for being there if the Greeks recognized him. As a result, he often wept bitterly. He wrote many piteous letters to her,—he could not be accused of sloth in this—beseeching her to keep her promise, since he was faithful, and to return to him. In pity, I think, Criseyde one day wrote him, as you may see, about her situation:

> Son of Cupid, example of goodness, sword of knight-hood, source of courtesy, how can a person suffering in

Book Five

hopeless torment and fear hope to send encouragement to you? I am without heart; I am sick; I am in distress! Since you cannot deal with me, nor I with you, I cannot send you heart or happiness. Your lengthy letters, neatly folded, have aroused the pity of my heart. I have also noticed that your letter was blotted with tears. You have demanded that I return, but that cannot yet be; for fear this letter will be intercepted, I now hesitate to explain why I cannot come. God knows that your unrest and impatience are grievous to me; you seem not to accept the orders of the gods rationally. It seems to me that the only thing you consider is your own pleasure. But do not be angry, I beseech you.

Slanderous tongues are the whole cause of my tarrying. I have heard more than I thought was known concerning how things stood between us two. I shall amend that situation by some dissimulation. Do not be angry, but I have heard how you are only deceiving me. But that does not matter—concerning you I can think only of trust and courtesy.

I shall return, but in my present difficulties I cannot say just what year or what day that will happen. However, I ask you for your respect and friendship always. For, truly, you may consider me a friend as long as I live. I pray you not to take ill that which I write so hastily. Where I am, I dare not write lengthy letters, and I really never knew how to write very well. Also, one can say much in a few words; the intention is everything, not the length of the letter. And now farewell; God keep you!

Your Criseyde

Troilus and Criseyde

When Troilus read this letter he found it very odd and sighed deeply. It seemed to him clear indication of a great change. In the end, however, he could not believe that Criseyde would not hold to that which she had promised him. For the man who loves well is unwilling to end love, even though it grieves him; nevertheless, it is said that at last, despite everything, the truth will become evident. Such an event happened to Troilus that he soon realized that Criseyde was not so kind to him as she should have been. Finally, he came to believe that, beyond doubt, all was lost for him.

One day Troilus was melancholy and full of suspicion of her for whom he planned to die. It happened, says the story, that a cloak was borne in front of Deiphebus through the streets of Troy, as the custom was, to signify his recent victory. This cloak, says Lollius, had been taken on the same day from Diomede by Deiphebus. When Troilus saw it he paid close attention, noticing its length and breadth and all the decorations. But as he examined it, his heart suddenly turned cold, for he saw on the collar the brooch which he had given to Criseyde on the morning she had to leave Troy, as a memento of him and his grief. She had pledged her faith to him that she would keep the pin forever! But he now realized well that she was no longer trustworthy. He went home and sent at once for Pandarus, to whom he told the whole story of the brooch, lamenting her changeable heart, his long love, his fidelity, and his punishment. Without further discussion, he cried out for death to bring him peace.

Troilus then spoke thus, "O my lady Criseyde, where are your faith and your promise? Where is your love? Where is your fidelity? Do you now find so much pleasure in Diomede?

Book Five

Alas, I would have thought that even if you decided not to keep your promise to me, at least you would not have deceived me! Who now can put faith in any oaths? Alas, until now I would never have thought that you could have changed so. No, even if I had sinned and done amiss, I would not have thought that your heart could have been cruel enough to slay me this way. Alas, your reputation for fidelity is now ruined, and that to me seems a pity.

"Was there no other brooch with which you could have bribed your new lover, except that one which I gave you with damp tears to remember me by? You had no other cause for your action, alas, except spite and the intention to show clearly your changed purpose. I now see that you have cast me clean out of your mind; yet for all this world I am unable to find in my heart the means of hating you for even a quarter of one day! Woe to me; I was born in an accursed time, in that I still love you, who cause me to suffer all this woe, best of all creatures.

"Now God, send me the favor of meeting Diomede! Truly, if I have strength and time, I shall make his sides bleed, I hope. O God, you should take the trouble of furthering fidelity and of punishing wrongs; why will you not take vengeance on this sin? Pandarus, you blamed me for trusting in dreams, and are accustomed to scold me often, but now you can see for yourself, if you wish, how faithful your niece, the fair Criseyde, is! God knows that in various ways the gods prophesy both joy and sorrow during sleep; my dream proves that. Certainly, without more discussion, from now on I shall seek my own death in the fighting as diligently as possible. I don't care how soon it comes! But truly, Criseyde, sweet maid whom I have served

A cloak was borne . . . through the streets of Troy

Troilus and Criseyde

with all my might, I have not deserved that which you have done to me."

Pandarus, who heard all this and thought that Troilus spoke truth, said not a word in opposition. He was sorry for his friend's grief and ashamed of his niece's sin. Because of these two factors, he stood as quiet as a stone; he knew no word to say. At last, however, he spoke, saying, "Dear brother, I can help you no further. What can I say? I certainly hate Criseyde, and, God knows, I will hate her forever! I did all that which you long ago asked me to do, without concern for my own honor or rest. If I did anything which pleased you, I am glad; and, God knows, this present treachery brings me grief. You can be sure that if I knew what to do I would gladly amend this grief to ease your spirit. I pray God to take her soon out of this world! I can say no more."

Great were the sorrow and laments of Troilus, but Fortune drove straight forward on her course. Criseyde loved the son of Tydeus and Troilus had to weep in cold grief. Such is the world to whoever understands it: there is in every situation little rest for the heart. God grant that we take it all for the best!

Troilus, the noble knight, showed his knighthood and his great strength in many a cruel battle, as one can read in the old books. No doubt, the Greeks paid dearly day and night for his anger. Always he sought out Diomede. I find that they met many times, with bloody strokes and fierce words, to test how well their spears were sharpened! God knows, Troilus beat upon Diomede's helmet with heavy stroke. Nevertheless, Fortune did not wish that either should die at the other's hands.

Book Five

If I had started out to write of the worthy Troilus' deeds at arms, then I would describe each of his battles. But I first began to write of his love, and I have told it as best I can. Whoever wishes to hear of his brave deeds can read Dares, who relates them all. I beseech every fair lady and every gentlewoman, whoever she is, not to be angry with me even though Criseyde was unfaithful. You can read of her sins in other books. If you wish, I would much prefer to write of Penelope's faith and of the good Alcestis. I do not say these things only for the sake of men, but rather on behalf of those women who are betrayed through false folk—may God send them sorrow, amen—who deceive you with great wit and subtlety. This thought leads me to speak and to pray all you women to beware of men and listen to what I say!—

Go, Little Book; go, my little tragedy; may God send your composer, before he dies, the power to compose a comedy! But, Little Book, do not envy any other poem; be humble before them all, and kiss the steps where you see Virgil, Ovid, Homer, Lucan, and Statius walking. Since there is such great diversity in English and in the writing of our language, I pray God that whoever copies you will not make errors in the words or the meters through faults in language. I pray God also that you will be understood, wherever you are read or sung. But back to the purpose of my earlier speech—

The Greeks paid dearly for the anger of Troilus, as I mentioned earlier. Thousands died at his hands, and, for all I can learn, he was without peer, except Hector, in his time. But, unfortunately, in accord with God's will, he was slain by the

Troilus and Criseyde

fierce Achilles. When he had been killed, his spirit happily rose to the eighth sphere, leaving every element behind. There he examined carefully the wandering stars, and listened to the harmony of their sounds filled with heavenly melody. Then he gazed down at this little spot of earth embraced by the sea, and despised fully this wretched world, holding it complete vanity in contrast to the true felicity which is in heaven above. At last, he looked at the spot on which he was killed, and within himself laughed at the grief of those who wept bitterly over his death. He condemned all our efforts in pursuit of blind lust, which is surely transitory, realizing that we should cast our hearts on heaven. Then, briefly, he went forth to that place where Mercury allotted him a dwelling. To such an end came Troilus because of love! To such an end came all his great worth! To such an end came his regal rank, his lust, and his nobility. To such an end comes the instability of this false world! And thus, as I have told, his love for Criseyde began, and thus he died.

O you young lusty folk, boys or girls, in whom love develops with age, flee homeward from worldly vanity. Cast your hearts upon that God who made you in his image, and remember that all this world is but a fair which passes as quickly as flowers die. Love Him who first died upon a cross to redeem our souls, then rose, and now sits in heaven above. For I dare say that He will betray no one who places his heart wholly on Him. Since He is the best and gentlest to love, what need is there to seek out feigned loves?

Here in this book you can learn of the pagans' old accursed rites and can see how little their gods avail. Here you can see the appetites of this wretched world and the final reward for

Book Five

the work of Jove, Apollo, Mars, and such rascals! Here you can see the form of the ancient writers' speech in poetry, as evidenced by their books.

O moral Gower, I direct this book to you, and to you, philosophical Strode, in the hope that you will kindly and zealously correct it where necessary.

To that steadfast Christ who died on the cross I pray for mercy with all my heart, and to the Lord I speak as follows: You eternal One, Two, Three, who reign forever in Three, Two, One, uncircumscribed you circumscribe all. Defend us from visible and invisible enemies, and in your mercy make each one of us, Jesus, worthy of your mercy, for the love of that kind maid, your Mother. Amen.

HERE ENDS THE BOOK OF TROILUS AND CRISEYDE

Selections in Middle English

Selections in Middle English

From the Original Poem

1. The Opening (I, 1-56)

1 The double sorwe of Troilus to tellen,
That was the kyng Priamus sone of Troye,
In lovynge, how his aventures fellen
Fro wo to wele, and after out of joie,
My purpos is, er that I parte fro ye.
Thesiphone, thow help me for t'endite
Thise woful vers, that wepen as I write.

To the clepe I, thow goddesse of torment,
Thow cruwel Furie, sorwynge evere yn peyne,
10 Help me, that am the sorwful instrument,
That helpeth loveres, as I kan, to pleyne.
For wel sit it, the sothe for to seyne,
A woful wight to han a drery feere,
And to a sorwful tale, a sory chere.

For I, that God of Loves servauntz serve,
Ne dar to Love, for myn unliklynesse,
Preyen for speed, al sholde I therfore sterve,
So fer am I from his help in derknesse.
But natheles, if this may don gladnesse
20 To any lovere, and his cause availle,
Have he my thonk, and myn be this travaille!

Selections in Middle English

But ye loveres, that bathen in gladnesse,
If any drope of pyte in yow be,
Remembreth yow on passed hevynesse
That ye han felt, and on the adversite
Of othere folk, and thynketh how that ye
Han felt that Love dorste yow displese,
Or ye han wonne hym with to gret an ese.

And preieth for hem that ben in the cas
30 Of Troilus, as ye may after here,
That Love hem brynge in hevene to solas;
And ek for me preieth to God so dere
That I have myght to shewe, in som manere,
Swich peyne and wo as Loves folk endure,
In Troilus unsely aventure.

And biddeth ek for hem that ben despeired
In love that nevere nyl recovered be,
And ek for hem that falsly ben apeired
Thorugh wikked tonges, be it he or she;
40 Thus biddeth God, for his benignite,
So graunte hem soone owt of this world to pace,
That ben despeired out of Loves grace.

And biddeth ek for hem that ben at ese,
That God hem graunte ay good perseveraunce,
And sende hem myght hire ladies so to plese
That it to Love be worship and plesaunce.
For so hope I my sowle best avaunce,
To prey for hem that Loves servauntz be,
And write hire wo, and lyve in charite,

Troilus and Criseyde

50   And for to have of hem compassioun,
      As though I were hire owne brother dere.
      Now herkneth with a good entencioun,
      For now wil I gon streght to my matere,
      In which ye may the double sorwes here
      Of Troilus in lovynge of Criseyde,
      And how that she forsook hym er she deyde.

2. Criseyde in the Temple (I, 169-182)

      Among thise othere folk was Criseyda,
170 In widewes habit blak; but natheles,
      Right as oure firste lettre is now an A,
      In beaute first so stood she, makeles.
      Hire goodly lokyng gladed al the prees.
      Nas nevere yet seyn thyng to ben preysed derre,
      Nor under cloude blak so bright a sterre
      As was Criseyde, as folk seyde everichone
      That hir behelden in hir blake wede.
      And yet she stood ful lowe and stille allone,
      Byhynden other folk, in litel brede,
180 And neigh the dore, ay undre shames drede,
      Simple of atir and debonaire of chere
      With ful assured lokyng and manere.

3. On Human Variety (II, 22-49)

      Ye knowe ek that in forme of speche is chaunge
      Withinne a thousand yeer, and wordes tho
      That hadden pris, now wonder nyce and straunge
      Us thinketh hem, and yet thei spake hem so,
      And spedde as wel in love as men now do;
      Ek for to wynnen love in sondry ages,
      In sondry londes, sondry ben usages.

Selections in Middle English

And forthi if it happe in any wyse,
30 That here be any lovere in this place
That herkneth, as the storie wol devise,
How Troilus com to his lady grace,
And thenketh, "so nold I nat love purchace,"
Or wondreth on his speche or his doynge,
I noot; but it is me no wonderynge.

For every wight which that to Rome went
Halt nat o path, or alwey o manere;
Ek in som lond were all the game shent,
If that they ferde in love as men don here,
40 As thus, in opyn doyng or in chere,
In visityng, in forme, or seyde hire sawes;
Forthi men seyn, ecch contree hath his lawes.

Ek scarsely ben ther in this place thre
That have in love seid lik, and don, in al;
For to thi purpos this may liken the,
And the right nought, yet al is seid or schal;
Ek som men grave in tree, some in ston wal,
As it bitit; but syn I have bigonne,
Myn auctour shal I folwen, if I konne.

4. Criseyde First Sees Troilus (II, 649-665)

Criseyda gan al his chere aspien,
650 And leet it so softe in hire herte synke,
That to hireself she seyde, "Who yaf me drynke?"

Troilus and Criseyde

For of hire owen thought she wex al reed,
Remembryng hire right thus, "Lo, this is he
Which that myn uncle swerith he moot be deed,
But I on hym have mercy and pitee."
And with that thought, for pure ashamed, she
Gan in hire hed to pulle, and that as faste,
Whil he and alle the peple forby paste;

And gan to caste and rollen up and down
660 Withinne hire thought his excellent prowesse,
And his estat, and also his renown,
His wit, his shap, and ek his gentilesse;
But moost hir favour was, for his distresse
Was al for hire, and thoughte it was a routhe
To sleen swich oon, if that he mente trouthe.

5. The Rainy Night at Pandarus' House (III, 1219-1253)

And now swetnesse semeth more swete,
1220 That bitternesse assaied was byforn;
For out of wo in blisse now they flete;
Non swich they felten syn that they were born.
Now is this bet than bothe two be lorn.
For love of God, take every womman heede
To werken thus, if it comth to the neede.

Criseyde, al quyt from every drede and tene,
As she that juste cause hadde hym to triste,
Made hym swich feste, it joye was to seene,
Whan she his trouthe and clene entente wiste;
1230 And as aboute a tree, with many a twiste,
Bytrent and writh the swote wodebynde,
Gan ech of hem in armes other wynde.

Selections in Middle English

And as the newe abaysed nyghtyngale,
That stynteth first whan she bygynneth to synge,
Whan that she hereth any herde tale,
Or in the hegges any wyght stirynge,
And after siker doth hire vois out rynge,
Right so Criseyde, whan hire drede stente,
Opned hire herte, and tolde hym hire entente.

1240 And right as he that seth his deth yshapen,
And dyen mot, in ought that he may gesse,
And sodeynly rescous doth hym escapen,
And from his deth is brought in sykernesse,
For al this world, in swych present gladnesse
Was Troilus, and hath his lady swete.
With worse hap God lat us nevere mete!

Hire armes smale, hire streghte bak and softe,
Hir sydes longe, flesshly, smothe, and white
He gan to stroke, and good thrift bad ful ofte
1250 Hire snowisshe throte, hire brestes rounde and lite:
Thus in this hevene he gan hym to delite,
And therwithal a thousand tyme hire kiste,
That what to don, for joie unnethe he wiste.

6. The Trojan Parliament (IV, 176-217)

Ector, which that wel the Grekis herde,
For Antenor how they wolde han Criseyde,
Gan it withstonde, and sobrely answerde:
"Syres, she nys no prisonere," he seyde;
180 "I not on yow who that this charge leyde,
But, on my part, ye may eftsone hem telle,
We usen here no wommen for to selle."

Troilus and Criseyde

The noyse of peple up stirte thanne at ones,
As breme as blase of straw iset on-fire;
For infortune it wolde, for the nones,
They sholden hire confusioun desire.
"Ector," quod they, "what goost may yow enspyre,
This womman thus to shilde, and don us leese
Daun Antenor—a wrong wey now ye chese—

190 "That is so wys and ek so bold baroun?
And we han nede of folk as men may se.
He is oon the grettest of this town.
O Ector, lat tho fantasies be!
O kyng Priam," quod they, "thus sygge we,
That al oure vois is to forgon Criseyde."
And to deliveren Antenor they preyde.

O Juvenal, lord! trewe is thy sentence,
That litel wyten folk what is to yerne
That they ne fynde in hire desir offence;
200 For cloude of errour lat hem nat discerne
What best is. And lo, here ensample as yerne:
This folk desiren now deliveraunce
Of Antenor, that brought hem to meschaunce.

For he was after traitour to the town
Of Troye; allas, they quytte hym out to rathe!
O nyce world, lo, thy discrecioun!
Criseyde, which that nevere dide hem scathe,
Shal now no lenger in hire blisse bathe;
But Antenor, he shal come hom to towne,
210 And she shal out; thus seyden here and howne.

Selections in Middle English

For which delibered was by parlement,
For Antenor to yelden out Criseyde,
And it pronounced by the president,
Altheigh that Ector "nay" ful ofte preyde.
And fynaly, what wight that it withseyde,
It was for nought; it moste ben and sholde,
For substaunce of the parlement it wolde.

7. The Parting (V, 15-91)

Ful redy was at prime Diomede
Criseyde unto the Grekis oost to lede,
For sorwe of which she felt hire herte blede,
As she that nyste what was best to rede.
And trewely, as men in bokes rede,
20   Men wiste nevere womman han the care,
Ne was so loth out of a town to fare.

This Troilus, withouten reed or loore,
As man that hath his joies ek forlore,
Was waytyng on his lady evere more
As she that was the sothfast crop and more
Of al his lust or joies herebifore.
But Troilus, now far-wel al thi joie,
For shaltow nevere sen hire eft in Troie!

Soth is that while he bood in his manere,
30   He gan his wo ful manly for to hide,
That wel unnethe it sene was in his chere;
But at the yate ther she sholde out ride,
With certeyn folk he hoved hire t'abide,
So wo-bigon, al wolde he naught hym pleyne,
That on his hors unnethe he sat for peyne.

Troilus and Criseyde

For ire he quook, so gan his herte gnawe,
Whan Diomede on horse gan hym dresse,
And seyde to hymself this ilke sawe:
"Allas!" quod he, "thus foul a wrecchednesse,
40 Whi suffre ich it? Whi nyl ich it redresse?
Were it nat bet atones for to dye
Than evere more in langour thus to drye?

"Whi nyl I make atones riche and pore
To have inough to doone, er that she go?
Why nyl I brynge al Troie upon a roore?
Whi nyl I slen this Diomede also?
Why nyl I rather with a man or two
Stele hire away? Whi wol I this endure?
Whi nyl I helpen to myn owen cure?"

50 But why he nolde don so fel a dede,
That shal I seyn, and whi hym liste it spare:
He hadde in herte alweyes a manere drede
Lest that Criseyde, in rumour of this fare,
Sholde han ben slayn; lo, this was al his care.
And ellis, certeyn, as I seyde yore,
He hadde it don, withouten wordes more.

Criseyde, whan she redy was to ride,
Ful sorwfully she sighte, and seyde "allas!"
But forth she moot, for aught that may bitide,
60 And forth she rit ful sorwfully a pas.
Ther is non other remedie in this cas.
What wonder is, though that hire sore smerte,
Whan she forgoth hire owen swete herte?

Selections in Middle English

This Troilus, in wise of curteysie,
With hauk on honde, and with an huge route
Of knyghtes, rood and did hire companye,
Passyng al the valeye fer withoute;
And ferther wolde han ridden, out of doute,
Ful fayn, and wo was hym to gon so sone;
70 But torne he moste, and it was ek to done.

And right with that was Antenor ycome
Out of the Grekis oost, and every wight
Was of it glad, and seyde he was welcome.
And Troilus, al nere his herte light,
He peyned hym with al his fulle myght
Hym to withholde of wepyng atte leeste,
And Antenor he kiste, and made feste.

And therwithal he moste his leve take,
And caste his eye upon hire pitously,
80 And neer he rood, his cause for to make,
To take hire by the honde al sobrely.
And Lord! so she gan wepen tendrely!
And he ful softe and sleighly gan hire seye,
"Now holde youre day, and do me nat to deye."

With that his courser torned he aboute
With face pale, and unto Diomede
No word he spak, ne non of al his route;
Of which the sone of Tideus took hede,
As he that koude more than the crede
90 In swich a craft, and by the reyne hire hente;
And Troilus to Troie homward he wente.

212

Troilus and Criseyde

8. The Triangle (V, 799-840)

This Diomede, as bokes us declare,
800 Was in his nedes prest and corageous,
With sterne vois and myghty lymes square,
Hardy, testif, strong, and chivalrous
Of dedes, lik his fader Tideus.
And some men seyn he was of tonge large;
And heir he was of Calydoigne and Arge.

Criseyde mene was of hire stature,
Therto of shap, of face, and ek of cheere,
Ther myghte ben no fairer creature.
And ofte tyme this was hire manere,
810 To gon ytressed with hire heres clere
Doun by hire coler at hire bak byhynde,
Which with a thred of gold she wolde bynde.

And, save hire browes joyneden yfere,
Ther nas no lak, in aught I kan espien.
But for to speken of hire eyen cleere,
Lo, trewely, they writen that hire syen,
That Paradis stood formed in hire yen.
And with hire riche beaute evere more
Strof love in hire ay, which of hem was more.

820 She sobre was, ek symple, and wys withal,
The best ynorisshed ek that myghte be,
And goodly of hire speche in general,
Charitable, estatlich, lusty, and fre;
Ne nevere mo ne lakked hire pite;
Tendre-herted, slydynge of corage;
But trewely, I kan nat telle hire age.

Selections in Middle English

And Troilus wel woxen was in highte,
And complet formed by proporcioun
So wel that kynde it nought amenden myghte;
830 Yong, fressh, strong, and hardy as lyoun;
Trewe as stiel in ech condicioun;
Oon of the beste entecched creature
That is, or shal, whil that the world may dure.

And certeynly in storye it is yfounde,
That Troilus was nevere unto no wight,
As in his tyme, in no degree secounde
In durryng don that longeth to a knyght.
Al myghte a geant passen hym of myght,
His herte ay with the first and with the beste
840 Stood paregal, to durre don that hym leste.

9. The Epilogue (V, 1786-1869)

Go, litel bok, go, litel myn tragedye,
Ther God thi makere yet, er that he dye,
So sende myght to make in som comedye!
But litel book, no makyng thow n'envie,
1790 But subgit be to alle poesye;
And kis the steppes, where as thow seest pace
Virgile, Ovide, Omer, Lucan, and Stace.

And for ther is so gret diversite
In Englissh and in writyng of oure tonge,
So prey I God that non myswrite the,
Ne the mysmetre for defaute of tonge.
And red wherso thow be, or elles songe,
That thow be understonde, God I biseche!
But yet to purpos of my rather speche.—

214

Troilus and Criseyde

1800 The wrath, as I bigan yow for to seye,
Of Troilus the Grekis boughten deere.
For thousandes his hondes maden deye,
As he that was withouten any peere,
Save Ector, in his tyme, as I kan heere.
But weilawey, save only Goddes wille!
Despitously hym slough the fierse Achille.

And whan that he was slayn in this manere,
His lighte goost ful blisfully is went
Up to the holughnesse of the eighthe spere,
1810 In convers letyng everich element;
And ther he saugh, with ful avysement,
The erratik sterres, herkenyng armonye
With sownes ful of hevenyssh melodie.

And down from thennes faste he gan avyse
This litel spot of erthe, that with the se
Embraced is, and fully gan despise
This wrecched world, and held al vanite
To respect of the pleyn felicite
That is in hevene above; and at the laste,
1820 Ther he was slayn, his lokyng down he caste.

And in hymself he lough right at the wo
Of hem that wepten for his deth so faste;
And dampned al oure werk that foloweth so
The blynde lust, the which that may nat laste,
And sholden al oure herte on heven caste.
And forth he wente, shortly for to telle,
Ther as Mercurye sorted hym to dwelle.

215

Selections in Middle English

Swich fyn hath, lo, this Troilus for love!
Swich fyn hath al his grete worthynesse!
1830 Swich fyn hath estat real above,
Swich fyn his lust, swich fyn hath his noblesse!
Swych fyn hath false worldes brotelnesse!
And thus bigan his lovyng of Criseyde,
As I have told, and in this wise he deyde.

O yonge, fresshe folkes, he or she,
In which that love up groweth with youre age,
Repeyreth hom fro worldly vanyte,
And of youre herte up casteth the visage
To thilke God that after his ymage
1840 Yow made, and thynketh al nys but a faire
This world, that passeth soone as floures faire.

And loveth hym, the which that right for love
Upon a crois, oure soules for to beye,
First starf, and roos, and sit in hevene above;
For he nyl falsen no wight, dar I seye,
That wol his herte al holly on hym leye.
And syn he best to love is, and most meke,
What nedeth feynede loves for to seke?

Lo here, of payens corsed olde rites,
1850 Lo here, what alle hire goddes may availle;
Lo here, thise wrecched worldes appetites;
Lo here, the fyn and guerdoun for travaille
Of Jove, Appollo, of Mars, of swich rascaille!
Lo here, the forme of olde clerkis speche
In poetrie, if ye hire bokes seche.

216

Troilus and Criseyde

O moral Gower, this book I directe
To the and to the, philosophical Strode,
To vouchen sauf, ther nede is, to correcte,
Of youre benignites and zeles goode.
1860   And to that sothefast Crist, that starf on rode,
With al myn herte of mercy evere I preye,
And to the Lord right thus I speke and seye:

Thow oon, and two, and thre, eterne on lyve,
That regnest ay in thre, and two, and oon,
Uncircumscript, and al maist circumscribe,
Us from visible and invisible foon
Defende, and to thy mercy, everichon,
So make us, Jesus, for thi mercy digne,
For love of mayde and moder thyn benigne.
Amen.

$$\frac{S}{i}$$